SURVIVAL: JAMESTOWN
First English Colony In America

In December, 1606, three ships set sail from England. On board were one hundred and fifty men. Before them lay the treacherous ocean, and awaiting them the trackless wilderness of Virginia. Under the leadership of Captain John Smith these men would face the rigors of nature, violent rivalries among themselves and the ever present threat of the powerful Indian tribes of the region. This is the dramatic story of the establishment of Jamestown and how the first English settlers fought for survival in the New World.

Books by Noel B. Gerson

THE LAST WILDERNESS
The Saga of America's Mountain Men

MR. MADISON'S WAR
1812—The Second War for Independence

ROCK OF FREEDOM
The Story of the Plymouth Colony

SURVIVAL: JAMESTOWN
First English Colony in America

Survival: Jamestown
FIRST ENGLISH COLONY IN AMERICA

by

Noel B. Gerson

Maps and drawings by Barry Martin

JULIAN MESSNER   **NEW YORK**

Published simultaneously in the United States and Canada by
Julian Messner, a division of Simon & Schuster, Inc.,
1 West 39 Street, New York, N.Y. 10018. All rights reserved.

Printed in the United States of America
Library of Congress Catalog Card No. 67-21619

For
Margot

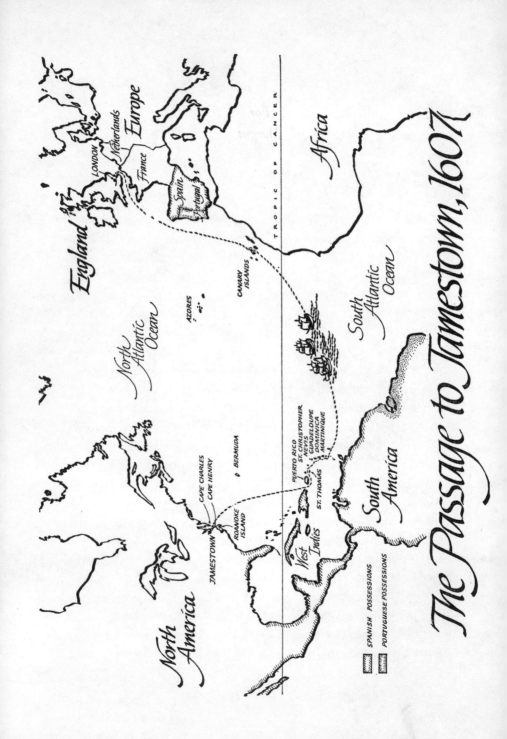

The Passage to Jamestown, 1607

I

"IF WE LIVE, this is a time we'll never forget." Ned Carson wearily lowered his woven Indian basket of clams and mussels to the ground and stared out past the Point, the tip of the long peninsula where the James River rushed to meet the Atlantic Ocean. "But if we die, it won't matter to anyone."

"Except to us, maybe." Thaddeus Warner wiped his sunbronzed forehead with the back of a sinewy arm.

With one accord the boys turned to stare at the Fort, a remarkably sturdy building of stone and wood that was a monument to the stubborn persistence of Captain John Smith. Its cannon commanded the sea approaches to America's first English colony and protected it from possible surprise attacks from the forest on the far side of the river. Two hundred yards behind the Fort stood the modest, thatch-roofed houses of Jamestown, neatly arranged in a square around a parade ground. There was a new church, too, erected on the ruins of the original house of worship that had been burned to the ground, a supply warehouse where armed guards stood sentry duty night and day to prevent looting, and, near the recently completed wharf, Captain Smith's sawmill.

A palisade of trimmed pine logs separated Jamestown proper from its fields of corn and wheat and barley, its vegetable patches and the fruit trees, planted by Smith the previous year, which had as yet produced no yield. Beyond the fields, cleared

7

with such effort by the little band of settlers, loomed the ever present forest, an unending sea of deep-green pine and hemlock, oak and beech, hickory and birch that stretched across the unexplored breadth of North America.

There was hatred in the eyes of Ned Carson and Thaddeus Warner as they gazed at the forest, but another emotion, difficult to define, also showed in their faces. The wilderness was their foe, cruel and harsh, yet John Smith had taught them that men who met it as equals, without fear, could draw sustenance from it. There were edible roots and berries, if one knew where to search for them. Wildfowl settled on hidden lakes and ponds, and animals provided meat, while their skins could be used for clothing and shoes. Shelters were fashioned from wood, and ropes from vines. The tallest hardwood trees were cut into lumber and shipped to England in return for the countless items, from gunpowder to iron kettles, from steel needles to blankets, that civilized men needed in this raw, primitive world.

Ned and Thaddeus despised their enemy, yet were mature enough to admire and respect it, too. It took life, but at the same time gave it. A man learned to acclimate to its ways, or perished. Ned and Thaddeus had survived, and with considerable justification believed they had become adults. They had been children of twelve when they left England on the great venture in 1606, and now, in the summer of 1609, they thought of themselves as men at the age of fifteen.

Many others had died, some of sickness, and the wilderness claimed still more. There had been sudden attacks by ruthless savages, months of near starvation, bungling by inept leaders who had quarreled among themselves. At one point the population of Jamestown dwindled to only fifty-eight men and boys but, thanks to the arrival of new settlers from England, climbed to one hundred and fifty again. In a sense, it was comforting to know the community was large enough to fight off a major Indian attack, but at the same time Thaddeus and Ned realized there were more mouths to feed. And food supplies were so perilously short that the dread of famine was ever present.

Ned shaded his eyes from the glare of the sun on the water as he peered up the James, searching in vain for the colony's schooner. "When Captain Smith comes back," he said, "we'll be sure to have a feast. There'll be fresh venison for roasting, and wild boar. If we're lucky, he'll have shot some bear and wild ducks, too."

"He always brings greens. And squash-melons." Thaddeus knew it was unwise to dwell on food, but couldn't resist. "Some of the lads who work in the cornfields were saying this morning that it's too early for squash, but the Captain knows where to find them."

Ned nodded gravely. "Everything will be fine again when he gets here."

Their faith in Smith was absolute, as unchanging as the brooding proximity of the forest. They knew, as did the other "commoners" of Jamestown, that the colony still existed only because of the leadership of the Captain, President of the Council and, in effect, Governor. The other Council members, who had so long deprived him of his rightful place in their midst, might be jealous of his power and envious of his accomplishments, but he had achieved what they could not. And if Jamestown continued to survive, he alone would be responsible.

Thaddeus hoisted his basket of mussels, clams and oysters onto his shoulder. "These need shelling and smoking before they spoil," he said. Experience had taught everyone in the little colony that food rotted quickly in the damp heat if it remained uncooked.

"Hold on." Ned dropped to one knee and studied a patch of tall grass that extended to the waterfront. "Look here." He pointed to some bent, matted grass and, beyond it, a scraped indentation in the mud on the riverbank. "Jamestown had some visitors last night."

Thaddeus joined him. "Chesapeake braves. Or Pamunkey, up to their old tricks. They knew they couldn't break in through the palisades, so they sent some warriors scouting on the open side."

Ned glanced contemptuously in the direction of the Fort. "The men on duty last night slept through it all, as usual. Captain Smith would sentence them to thirty days in jail for being so careless." He stood again, his face bleak. "If we don't tighten our defenses the Pamunkey will try another sneak raid."

Thaddeus remembered that three colonists had been wounded when a party of Pamunkey braves had made an attempt to loot the town. "Captain Ratcliffe is in charge this week." He picked up his basket again.

It was unnecessary for Ned to reply, and his expression became still more glum. John Ratcliffe had been a sea captain, the commander of one of the three vessels that carried the original colonists from England to the New World. He had remained in Jamestown, certain that eventually he would find gold, silver and gems that would make him wealthy, and in the meantime had proved himself a troublemaker on the Council.

The boys trudged in silence toward the parade ground. At one end were stone-lined pits, where several men were smoking fish and three or four wild geese that the colonists assigned to hunting duty had brought down that morning. The catch was pitifully small, but hungry men learned to be grateful for scraps.

Thaddeus dumped his basket and turned to his friend. "Come with me while I report to Ratcliffe."

Ned was convinced he would be wasting his time, but agreed, and they walked together toward the houses of the Council members, across the parade ground from the pits. There was no sign of Ratcliffe in the tiny dwelling he shared with another of the leaders, Gabriel Archer, and Thaddeus decided to wait until later in the day. Suddenly, however, he became aware of something unusual off to his right, and grasped his companion's arm.

Both boys looked apprehensively in the direction of the main warehouse, which was located only a few paces from the leaders' cottages. The two guards who stood sentry duty at the entrance were gone, which was extraordinary, and the door was open, which was shocking. It was Captain Smith's strict, inviolable rule that no one could go into the warehouse unless four members of the Council were present.

As Thaddeus and Ned watched, uncertain whether to stay or go off for help, John Ratcliffe emerged. A lean, sallow-skinned man with a thin face and prematurely gray hair, he carried a wooden gourd filled with parched corn in one hand and a large chunk of jerked venison in the other. Reacting instinctively, he started to hide the food behind his back, but recovered swiftly. Kicking the door shut behind him, he decided to bluster.

"You know you aren't allowed near this building," he said. "Leave at once, or I'll bring formal charges against you."

Thaddeus was too numb to speak. Although it was true that

food had grown scarce, a rumor, repeated many times in recent weeks, appeared to be true: some members of the Council, who had access to the warehouse, were stealing more than their fair share of the meager stores.

Ned gulped and took a deep breath. "Sir," he said, "we've been looking for you. Some Pamunkey—or maybe they were Chesapeake—landed on the peninsula last night and scouted near the fort."

"You ought to know that military information should be reported to the lieutenant of the guard," Ratcliffe snapped.

The boys had no alternative and rapidly walked away. Ned, the bolder of the pair, glanced back over his shoulder and saw Ratcliffe hurrying toward his cottage with the stolen food. "We've got to keep quiet about this," he muttered. "It's our word against Ratcliffe's, and you know who'll win. What's more, the men might riot, and we'd be blamed for that, too."

Thaddeus nodded, and wondered if they could trust anyone in a position of authority. "I hope," he said, making a supreme effort to curb his feeling of hysteria, "that Captain Smith gets back to Jamestown before it's too late."

In the virtually unanimous opinion of the Jamestown colonists, Gabriel Archer's high opinion of himself was unjustified. He was a handsome, slender man, to be sure, and had traveled to the New World with such a wardrobe that he still managed an elegant appearance while others dressed in rags. But he had no other known attributes, and the residents of Jamestown were convinced that his glib tongue alone had persuaded the financial sponsors of the colony to grant him a place on the ruling Council. He brashly proclaimed himself a military expert, but his title of "Captain" was self-assumed. On one notable occasion, when his advice on matters of defense had been particularly foolish, John Smith publicly accused him of inventing the claim that he had served as a mercenary officer with the Dutch in their long and bitter war with France.

But no one could claim that Archer lacked courage. With the President absent from Jamestown on an extended visit to the interior to find meat and grain, Archer decided to solve the problem of the food shortage in his own way. Taking no one into his confidence, he donned his shirt of chain mail, a breastplate and a helmet of steel, and marched off into the wilderness with twenty of the colony's most experienced fighting men, whom he armed with muskets, pistols and swords.

No one in the party knew his destination as he led the company on foot through an endless maze of towering trees and thick underbrush. His sense of direction was faulty, and four different times he doubled back on his tracks, but by the afternoon of the second day out of Jamestown it dawned on the men that he was taking them to the principal village of the Chickahominy, the capital of the great sachem, Powhatan, who ruled a vast confederation of Indian tribes.

The colonists exchanged uneasy glances, and the same thought was in every mind. Captain Smith, who had made it his business to learn the language and understand the character of the savages, had established excellent relationships with the powerful Chickahominy. His barter deals, in which he exchanged knives and blankets, iron skillets and axes for corn and meat, had always been as fair to the Indians as to the settlers, and he had refused to cheat the natives by palming off worthless beads and other trinkets on them. He refrained from using or threatening force, even though he had once been taken prisoner by the Chickahominy and narrowly escaped being stoned to death. He had taken care to treat Powhatan with a respect that would have tried the patience of lesser men, and consequently won the friendship of the chief.

Powhatan made an informal but binding peace treaty with Smith, an agreement that had saved Jamestown from extermination, since the Chickahominy were capable of sending several thousand warriors into battle. Equally important, Powhatan supplied the colony with corn, dried squash and venison on a regular basis in return for some of civilization's products. These provisions, although insufficient for Jamestown's needs, nevertheless saved the colony when their own crops failed and game proved scarce.

Common sense had dictated that Smith alone take charge of the delicately balanced relations, and no other member of the Council had been stupid enough to interfere with an arrangement that had proved mutually satisfactory to both Englishmen and Chickahominy. Now, however, Archer was deliberately risking catastrophe by taking matters into his own hands.

Unseen warriors concealed in the forest about two miles from the sachem's village identified the visitors, appeared in the open and conducted them to the community situated on a high bluff overlooking a swift-flowing tributary of the James River. Cultivated fields were located outside the village, and squaws in shapeless buckskins or lighter garments made of woven reeds worked in cornfields and bean patches. Small, naked children played at the feet of the women, and dogs ran to greet the visitors.

Other braves appeared, seemingly from nowhere, to fall in beside the small company, and when they reached the dusty clearing, still more dogs raced up to the Englishmen, barking and cavorting. Archer maintained his dignity, however, as he led the column past the mud huts and communal cooking pits of the married braves and squaws, and up the hill toward the long-houses occupied by the single warriors, adolescent boys and unmarried women. Elders squatting on the ground outside huts regarded the strangers impassively, while a few squaws too old to work indicated the true feelings of the tribe by spitting.

About two thirds of the way up the bluff stood a complex of huts larger than the rest, with animal skins that served as a door and window flaps. These buildings were the headquarters of Powhatan, his three wives, his many sons, and his one daughter, Pocahontas, to whom Smith had loaned a copy of the Bible and who was painstakingly learning to speak English.

Powhatan came out of the largest hut, a powerfully built savage with alert, intelligent eyes. He wore a feathered cape, a badge of his office, over his buckskin loincloth. As he advanced several paces toward the visitors, only a flicker indicated his surprise that Smith was not a member of the party. He greeted the Englishmen with elaborate courtesy.

When it was discovered that none of the colonists spoke the tongue of the Chickahominy, the sachem sent for his daughter, an exceptionally pretty child of about eleven years, with delicate features and a natural, easy grace. Pocahontas laughed with pleasure when she first saw the men she considered friends, but her smile faded as Archer launched into a long, nasty harangue.

The essence of his argument was simple. Jamestown was hungry, while the Chickahominy storehouses were filled. He wanted ample supplies, and if amicable arrangements couldn't be made, he intended to take meat and grain by force. The other colonists were horrified, and Pocahontas became so flustered she forgot to translate his words.

But he managed to convey his meaning to Powhatan, who

quietly signaled one of his sons. In a few moments the Englishmen were surrounded by scores of warriors armed with spears, bone-handled knives and axes.

Gabriel Archer demonstrated his brute courage as well as his lack of discretion by drawing a pistol and holding the muzzle a few inches from Powhatan's chest. Any threat against the sachem was considered a gross insult, and inasmuch as the savages were terrified of firearms, the gesture was even more offensive.

Archer laughed, pointed the pistol into the air and fired it. Some of the warriors cringed, shrank from the Englishmen and covered their ears with their hands. But Archer knew precisely what he was doing, and handed the pistol, still smoking, to Powhatan.

An expression of greed spread across the sachem's face, and he was overjoyed when Archer gave him the other pistol as well, together with a bag of powder and another of lead bullets.

Precisely as Archer had anticipated, Powhatan ordered his storehouses opened. But the sachem drove a hard bargain, and gave the settlers only twenty sacks of corn and four sides of venison in return for the weapons.

Archer became annoyed, and would have protested violently had his own subordinates not silenced him. The colonists were aghast at the damage he had already done, and were determined not to let him make matters worse.

His gift of pistols, ammunition and gunpowder brought him a reasonable quantity of supplies in return, but the price was far greater than Jamestown could afford to pay. For two years, ever since landing in the territory called Virginia, the colonists had obeyed a basic, unalterable decree. John Smith, who had not been in a position of authority at the time, suggested that it would be insane to let the savages gain possession of firearms.

His thought was so sensible that Captain Christopher Newport, commodore of the expedition, agreed at once, and so had the members of the Council, who had not even felt it necessary to discuss the matter. A tiny band of Englishmen facing countless savages, all of them potential foes, in a wild, alien land, could survive only if they allowed no pistols, muskets or cannon to fall into the hands of the Indians.

The rule had been so fundamental to the safety of the colony that every President had insisted it be enforced to the letter. Only once had an attempt been made to disobey the law. Soon after Smith had taken office he had discovered that two of the settlers were planning to sell a musket to the Chesapeake. He had taken such a grave view of the affair that he ordered the men whipped at the post, and soon thereafter, when Captain Newport returned to the New World on one of his frequent voyages, he took the pair back to England in chains.

Now Gabriel Archer had not only broken the rule but had set a precedent that would cause the Chickahominy, as well as all the lesser tribes, to clamor for firearms. The injunction that had been Jamestown's primary protection had been discarded, and the future would be unimaginably hazardous.

It was small wonder that senior warriors, mature men who had faced death many times, leaped and shouted like schoolboys. And the twenty Englishmen clustered in the forest clearing so far from home could guess what was going through the mind of Powhatan as the sachem lovingly stroked the brace of pistols and fondled the bullets. Powhatan, at least, believed the colonists' strict policy had collapsed, felt certain that henceforth he could obtain more of the potent "firesticks" in return for the provisions the colonists so desperately needed.

Archer, short-sighted and complacent, quickly conquered his disappointment and was pleased, too. Scarcely aware of his companions' disgust and rage, he pictured for himself the hero's welcome that awaited him when his company marched through the gates of Jamestown laden with corn and venison. He had grown heartily sick of the adulation the settlers bestowed on Smith, and now, at last, it would be his turn to bask in popular favor. Perhaps, with the help of other Council members, he could force the election of a new President before Smith's present one-year term expired.

After serving as head of the Jamestown government for a year or two, Archer thought, he would return to England. The wealthy nobles who had sponsored the colony would be eager to present him at court because he would give them the kind of administration they craved. He was familiar with their letters complaining that too much attention was being devoted to agricultural pursuits, and he sympathized with their desire for gold. Somewhere in this huge wilderness there had to be gold, and once he freed the settlers from the need to find food, they would be able to devote all their efforts to the search for precious metals.

It wasn't too much to hope that King James I would knight him. It would be good to be called Sir Gabriel. Archer liked the sound.

Dreams of the future still filled his mind as, refusing Powhatan's invitation to spend the night in the Chickahominy village, he set out for Jamestown at the head of his little company. The men were unusually silent on the march, and he assumed they were sullen because of the grain and meat they were forced to carry.

What he didn't know was that the settlers realized, far more accurately than did he, the enormity of the act he had perpetrated. A radical change had been made in Jamestown's trading pattern with the Indians, and the perils of life in the wilderness were greatly increased. Only one hope remained, and the colonists clung to it desperately: perhaps Captain Smith could transform potential tragedy into victory, as he had done so often in the past. He alone was capable of finding some way to prevent the savages from gaining possession of firearms while continuing to obtain vital food supplies from them. If he failed, Jamestown was doomed, but their faith in him was unlimited.

While the latest in Jamestown's unending series of crises boiled at the colony's site, the bearded, energetic Captain John Smith was completing his trip of exploration into the interior of the New World. Bareheaded and dressed in a deerskin shirt and trousers, he stood near the prow of the schooner as it glided silently down the James River. Holding a sketching pad in one hand, he checked the details of the map he had made on the voyage upstream, and satisfied himself that his drawings were accurate.

He had good reason to feel pleased with the results of his journey. He had sailed more than one hundred miles inland with his seven companions and traveled another fifty miles on foot. Not only had he achieved the deepest penetration of the North American continent ever accomplished by an Englishman, but he had mapped the area accurately, just as he had previously mapped Chesapeake Bay, the Potomac River and a portion of the mighty Susquehanna River. His maps, together with the book he was writing from his careful notes, would provide England with eagerly sought information about tens of thousands of square miles of this unknown land of omnipresent forests.

In spite of all he had done, however, Smith felt restless and gloomy. He had found the peace he himself craved in this magnificent wilderness, yet he knew there was no peace for Jamestown. Sir Walter Raleigh and even Henry, Prince of Wales and heir to the British crown, had warned him that the colony was an ill-conceived venture, but he hadn't been able to believe them. Now he knew better, and his task, his responsibilities, were almost too great for one man to bear.

Looking back, he could see that the basic fault lay with the Earl of Southampton and the other great lords who financed this expedition. The nobles were interested only in becoming wealthier, in accumulating the gold and diamonds of the New World. They had repeatedly threatened to withdraw their support unless he concentrated on a search for minerals, and they seemed incapable of understanding his explanation that the real riches of America lay in her black soil and superb forests.

No colony could succeed unless its sponsors thought in terms of establishing a permanent settlement. Certainly Jamestown would fail unless wives and sweethearts joined the all-male population. It would be necessary for families to sink their roots deep in the New World, grow their own food and become self-sufficient. Until this basic issue was resolved, the colonists would be temporary visitors in Virginia.

Other problems were even more urgent. Through a series of barter deals with the various tribes he encountered in the interior, he had obtained enough sacks of corn, hogsheads of beans and bales of dried meat to satisfy the colony's immediate need for provisions. But the solution was not a permanent one, and he knew the settlers had to clear more land and plant far greater quantities of crops this spring if they hoped to survive.

Jamestown's relations with the savages were critical, too. Smith gleaned from some of the natives he met that the Pamunkey and Chesapeake were planning to launch major attacks on the settlement before summer came. Since a war would not only cost many lives but permanently sour Jamestown's relations with two of the area's leading tribes, Smith had come to the conclusion that he would have to take preventive measures. He would invite all the chiefs of the region to a military review, and would squander some of his precious gunpowder by firing his cannon as well as his company's muskets for their benefit.

He could only hope the chiefs would be sufficiently impressed to abandon their scheme. At least it was a relief to realize his friendship with the Chickahominy was secure. If Powhatan should demand or obtain firearms, life would become infinitely more complicated, but he put the thought out of his mind. There were already too many concrete difficulties to be handled.

One of the worst was the damage his colleagues on the Council might have done during his absence. Perhaps he was borrowing trouble, but he had learned from bitter experience that the other members schemed, connived against him and stirred up trouble whenever he went on a journey. None of them seemed to realize it was imperative that they work together for the mutual good of the community. Captain Newport had carried reports back to London explaining in detail that the men selected by the sponsors to lead the colony were inept and selfish, but only two had returned to England since the initial founding of Jamestown, and their replacements had been greedy bumblers, too.

Correcting his drawing of a bend in the river, Smith sighed. He was tired, more exhausted than he had ever been in an active life as a soldier of fortune and explorer. It seemed too much to hope that the financiers in London would send competent officers to administer the affairs of Jamestown, but if they did not, he would have to continue carrying the burden alone, and he was afraid it was more than he could bear.

He was so lost in thought he failed to notice that a stiff breeze had sprung up, and he was surprised when one of his crew broke into his solitude to ask him whether he wanted sail hauled in. The man was smoking a pipe, a custom picked up from the savages, and the wind was sending a shower of burning tobacco across the deck.

Before Smith could rebuke him for his carelessness, a spark landed on the bag of gunpowder stowed near the prow. The Captain reacted instantly to the danger and threw himself onto the bag, hoping to smother the spark. But he was too late. There was a sudden flash, then a roar that shook the ship, and John Smith was enveloped in flames.

Fright paralyzed the crew, and Smith, in spite of his excruciating agony, took charge. At his shouted command the men lowered buckets into the river and drenched him with the contents. Again and again they hauled up water, and it seemed an eternity before the fire was extinguished.

Then, but only then, did Smith lose consciousness. The one man on whom the entire future of the Jamestown colony depended lay in a coma, badly burned, more dead than alive.

II

LONDON, IN THE YEAR 1606, was the most exciting city in the civilized world. Captain John Smith, who had just returned to the capital of his native land, had become an expert on the subject after spending ten years as a mercenary soldier and traveler in distant places, and he was convinced that London was unique. He knew Paris and Rome, Vienna and Prague and Budapest; he had spent six months in Constantinople as a prisoner of the Turks, and he was one of the few Englishmen of his time who had visited Moscow and journeyed through Russia.

It was a joy to stroll once again through the bustling streets of London. At Whitehall, the palace of King James I, pikemen in steel corselets and burnished helmets stood at rigid attention outside the gates, and John regarded them with the professional eye of a fighting man who had achieved international renown in the long campaign of the Austrians to drive the infidel Turks from Christendom. English soldiers, he thought proudly, were capable of meeting any challenge.

Scores of ships rode at anchor in the River Thames, reflecting England's growing trade with Europe, India and the remote Orient. One of the vessels was the bark of Smith's old friend, Henry Hudson, himself recently returned from a long voyage to the East Indies, and their reunion would be an occasion to remember.

The Strand, London's busiest thoroughfare, was alive with traffic. Gentlemen in plumed hats and silk capes rode with reckless abandon, their mounts grazing the vendors of meat pies, chestnuts and grilled oysters who were selling their wares to a seemingly endless flow of pedestrians. Great lords and their ladies were protected from the throngs by the glass windows of their gilded carriages, which were drawn by teams of matched horses, and a few nobles were enjoying the novelty of riding in sedan chairs, enclosed boxes with a seat and windows which were carried on the shoulders of servants in livery.

Smith caught a glimpse of the Tower, London's ancient

fortress that was now used as a prison, and a momentary chill marred the joy of his return to the land of his birth. The first news he had heard after landing in the country two days earlier was that Sir Walter Raleigh, the distinguished diplomat, sailor and patron of the New World land he called Virginia in honor of the late Queen Elizabeth I, was being held in the Tower by King James on unspecified charges. Englishmen enjoyed a greater freedom than any other people on earth, but still had to tread warily.

The solid gray piles of the Temples, the nation's law courts, spread up Fleet Street, a further reminder that liberty was relative, and Smith promised himself he would keep out of trouble with the authorities. His days of adventure were behind him; he had returned to England with a small fortune he intended to invest wisely, and he was ready to settle down.

As he entered a modest building with bay windows and leaded panes, he wondered anew why Archdeacon Richard Hakluyt had summoned him to a conference. Smith knew only that the clergyman, the Archdeacon of Westminster, was the nation's leading geographer and had developed a passionate interest in the virtually unknown and unexplored continent of North America. Why such a man should want to see someone who had spent the better part of ten years in the farther reaches of Europe made no sense.

Hakluyt, a gentle man with the wise eyes and mild manner of a scholar, was in no hurry to explain. He received his guest in an oak-paneled chamber, and soon was joined by a broad-shouldered young man in a suit of unpretentious but expensively cut wool whom Hakluyt did not introduce. They sipped mulled cider before a roaring fire, and Hakluyt complimented Smith at length on the sketches and maps he had drawn of eastern Europe, regions never before charted by an Englishman. Finding it difficult to believe that anyone could have become such an expert cartographer without formal training, the Archdeacon drew out his guest on his many adventures, and the husky young man listened carefully, but said nothing.

At last Hakluyt came to the point of the interview. "Have you ever thought of making a voyage to the New World?"

Smith smiled and shook his head. "I've come home to stay."

"I'd think you'd find the challenge irresistible," Hakluyt replied. "A great continent—larger, I believe, than anyone dreams —is waiting to be explored and mapped. I'll tell you a secret, Captain. A group of investors has obtained a patent from King James to establish a colony in America, preferably in the region known as Virginia. A great many men have volunteered for the expedition, but there's a need for leaders. Someone with your qualifications as a military man and sailor would be unique."

Smith remained polite. "I've heard it said that Raleigh rots in a cell because he couldn't satisfy King James' lust for New World gold. I have enough to keep me in modest comfort for the rest of my days, and I plan to write the story of my travels."

Hakluyt was undismayed. "You could write about far more after visiting Virginia. And although I'll grant you that most of our investors want gold and gems, there are a few of us who are fascinated by exploration for its own sake. Take some of my charts with you, even though I must apologize for their inaccuracy. They may persuade you to change your mind." He spoke at length, glowingly, of the rivers and mountain ranges, valleys and plateaus awaiting discovery in America, and of the enduring fame that would be achieved by the man who found them.

Smith was fascinated, but did not waver. "I'd like to study

your charts, and I thank you for the privilege. After I've learned more of the venture, perhaps I could be persuaded to make a small investment in it myself. But I refuse to give James the chance to become my jailer."

The silent young man spoke for the first time. "I can guarantee your safety. We need a man of your talents."

Hakluyt smiled quietly. "His Royal Highness is a man of his word."

Smith felt the color rush to his face. He should have known that the young man was Prince Henry, James' elder son, and realized he would be on his way to prison at this very moment if the heir to the throne were a petty man. He started to stammer an apology.

The Prince of Wales held up a hand. "Say no more, Captain. Between us, my father can be very difficult, but he isn't standing behind this expedition. I am, and I'd go myself if the Privy Council hadn't forbidden me to leave England. I can only beg you not to reject our offer too abruptly. Think about it, and learn what little there is to know about the New World. If you wish, I'll make arrangements for you to talk with the few men who have been there. Our generation, yours and mine, faces the greatest challenge in history, and I hope you'll help England meet it."

In the weeks that followed, Smith conferred many times with Archdeacon Hakluyt, and gradually fell under the great geographer's spell. He heard the legends of the colony founded by Sir Walter Raleigh in Virginia that had vanished from the face of the earth overnight. Like others before him, he speculated on the possibility that it had been attacked by savage natives.

At Hakluyt's house he met a number of sea captains who had made voyages to New World waters. Among them was the bluff, handsome Bartholomew Gosnold, who had sailed hundreds of miles along the North American coast in 1602 and had gone ashore on several occasions.

"I've never seen a land like it," Gosnold said, prodded by Hakluyt's questions. "There are trees everywhere, literally millions of them. In the north are the tallest, strongest oaks on earth. The maples are magnificent, and the elms are twice the size of ours. As for the pines, well, there must be a dozen different kinds."

Smith felt his own interest sparking, and tried to picture the vast forest. "Is it as quiet there as in the woods of Yorkshire?"

Gosnold tried to explain. "At first, you think it's silent. But if you're very still, you discover the wildnerness is alive. Small animals creep through the brush, and there's more large game than you can imagine. There are birds, too, thousands of them. I'm not very good at describing things, but I know there are types that have never been seen in England or Europe."

Hakluyt broke into the conversation. "A man with your talents as an artist, Captain Smith, could make a tremendous contribution to science. You could sketch animals and birds completely unknown in the civilized world."

Smith could feel himself weakening.

"The New World gets into the blood of everyone who has been there," Gosnold said. "I've never cared much for cards or dice, but I can understand why some men must spend all their time gambling."

Smith nodded. He knew, too, that some lures were irresistible, and thought of soldiers who had been unable to cure a craving for strong alcoholic spirits, even though drink ruined them.

"Gambling," Gosnold said, "is a diseased magnet. The New World is a healthy one. I sometimes find myself dreaming of

those forests at night, and so do the lads who sailed with me
four years ago. That's why I'm going back."

"You're joining this expedition?"

"Of course I'm commanding one of the company's ships.
I wouldn't miss this voyage if my life depended on it!"

Smith wondered if he could afford to miss the opportunity
that had been offered to him.

Henry Hudson was a grave, rawboned man who seldom smiled,
dressed in somber clothes and looked more like a clergyman
than a successful mariner who had spent more than twenty
years at sea. But he was at home in the crowded tavern on the
Thames waterfront frequented by ships' masters and their mates,
and he shook hands with a score of acquaintants before leading Captain Smith to a secluded table at the rear of the establishment.

"John," he said to his old friend, "I want you to give me your
word you won't repeat what I'm going to say to you."

Smith obligingly swore an oath.

Captain Hudson relaxed and stared up at the oak beams of
the old tavern. "When you and I were boys, our heroes were
admirals like Sir Francis Drake and John Hawkins. We dreamed
of following their example. That was a long time ago, and
since then we've traveled, between us, all over the face of the
known earth." Suddenly he sat erect and pointed a long finger
at his companion. "Are you satisfied with what you've done?"

"I thought I was when I came back to England," Smith con-
fessed, "but now I'm not so sure."

Hudson's face creased in one of his infrequent grins. "Archdeacon Hakluyt is a persuasive man."

"Are you going to Virginia?"

Henry Hudson shook his head. "No, I'm planning a scheme

of my own." He went on to explain that he had been studying with Hakluyt for a long time and also had been corresponding at length with Peter Plancius, the distinguished Dutch geographer. England and all the nations of Europe, he said, were engaging in an ever increasing trade with the "pepper islands" of the East Indies and with the fabulously wealthy land of Cathay, which some called China.

A fortune awaited those who discovered a short sea route to the East, Hudson said. He himself had little interest in riches, as such, but was thirsty for the joy of making the discovery for its own sake.

Two voyages he had made into the western reaches of the Atlantic in his youth convinced him there was an open water route to the East through the North American continent. Hakluyt and Plancius, although less certain, agreed with the possibility, and were gathering charts and ships' logs for him. The maps were vague, and the few notes scribbled by the masters of fishing vessels were even less informative; but he intended to let nothing deter him and planned to make a definitive voyage of exploration after he gleaned all he could learn on the subject.

"I'm hoping," he said, "that someone who goes to Virginia will make some sketches of the rivers there for me."

Smith felt himself being manipulated by forces beyond his control. "Map-making has been my hobby for some years. I took it up when I discovered that most maps are shoddy. Men who make them rely more on their imagination than on the facts of geography."

"Hakluyt showed me your sketches of Russia, Transylvania and the Macedonian hill country of Greece. He says they're the best he's ever seen."

There was a long silence. "If I should go to Virginia with the

Jamestown company," Smith said at last, "I might be able to make some maps that would be helpful to you."

"To me, to our trading interests and to the crown. We live," Hudson said, his thoughts remarkably similar to those of Prince Henry, "in an age when knowledge is important for its own sake. Our generation is getting rid of the ignorance that has hampered civilization for thousands of years. Think of it! There are unknown lands all over the earth, uncharted seas and rivers no civilized man has ever seen. And after all these centuries, we're the people who are going to find them. What a wonderful time to be alive!"

Smith felt the desire to join the Virginia expedition growing increasingly irresistible.

The Tower of London had been bult at a time when men still used catapults, battering rams and bows and arrows to defend themselves. But even in an age of gunpowder it was a massive, impregnable structure. Its walls were reassuringly thick, and sentries stationed on its high ramparts could see all of London and the surrounding countryside. Even though it was no longer used for the protection of the city, the citizens of London were soothed by its presence.

Once inside its walls, however, the atmosphere changed. Officers with swords at their sides and pistols in their belts roamed the ancient structure day and night. Guards armed with steel-tipped pikes were stationed in pairs at every landing. The corridors were dark, and the flickering torches set at intervals in wall niches merely accented the gloom. Perhaps the most distinctive feature of the place was its quiet. No one shouted, the guards were not allowed to speak, and the officers rarely conversed with one another. There was no sound but the soft thud of leather boots on the worn stones and the faint, metallic clink of the deputy warden's keys. The Tower was used exclusively as a prison, and no one could enter it without feeling its confining presence.

John Smith followed the deputy warden up a narrow, winding staircase to a thick door of oak, studded with iron, and after a heavy bolt was removed, a key grated in a lock. The door creaked open, and Smith hesitantly walked into the anteroom of the apartment occupied by the Tower's most renowned captive. A manservant appeared and conducted the visitor to a large room that, at first glance, resembled a private library or study. Books were piled high on tables and filled several cases, and papers filled with notes littered other tables and a desk.

But the real nature of the place quickly became apparent. In spite of the thick Turkish rug on the floor and the miniatures painted in oil of an attractive lady and several children on the desk, the walls of dark gray stone were forbidding and stark. Thick bars of iron set twelve inches apart were set in the frames of the high windows, and a mesh of steel covered the one small window out of which an occupant could look down on the River Thames.

The man seated behind the desk, who was writing furiously with a quill pen when Smith entered the chamber, looked up, smiled and stood. He was so completely at ease that he more nearly resembled a gracious host than a prisoner of state. It had often been said that Sir Walter Raleigh was too handsome and elegant for his own good, and not even a long stay in the Tower had spoiled his charm. His face, above the pointed, slightly old-fashioned beard that made him resemble Lucifer, was animated. His breeches and doublet of green velvet, trimmed with gold buttons, had cost a small fortune, and the gold buckles on his shoes were worth another. He appeared to be in excellent health, although he was pale; and he moved with the coordinated grace of one who had been physically active all of his life. It was difficult to believe he was more than fifty years old.

He welcomed Smith warmly, made him comfortable in a cushioned chair and sent his servant for two mugs of sack. "You risk much by coming to see me, Captain. King James doesn't look with favor on my visitors."

Smith explained the reasons for his call. Sir Walter had sent out several expeditions to the New World, and had himself made a voyage to South America, where he had conducted a vigorous but unsuccessful search for gold. He knew much about the lands on the far shores of the Atlantic, and Smith wanted his advice. As one who had himself visited many distant lands, he wanted to know whether it was true that the New World was unlike any other part of the earth.

"It's unique," Raleigh replied instantly. "The forests are beyond imagination."

The Captain wanted to know why everyone who had seen America dwelled so incessantly on the subject of the forests.

Sir Walter was never at a lost for words, but voiced his thoughts carefully. "Their beauty is staggering, but there aren't many who are impressed by sheer beauty. The forests are terrifying. When you plunge into them, you feel as though they'll swallow you up alive. It's something like being thrown into a huge sea and being afraid you'll drown."

Smith, who had twice been shipwrecked, thought he understood.

"Men react in one of two ways to the forests of the New World," Raleigh continued. "Some are so completely overwhelmed that the forests defeat them. I'm not speaking now only of the cowards. Men who are strong and have shown their courage sometimes buckle in the wilderness. The forests can be barbarous and romantic at the same time. Some men become bewildered."

The Captain hoped he was strong enough to meet the test.

"Others rise to the challenge. I'll never forget a poet who sailed with me to America. He was a sensitive, timid lad, but there was something primitive in his nature that responded to the savage quality of the forests. He not only survived, but flourished, while men who were capable of tearing him apart with their bare hands crumpled. One went mad, and others died." Suddenly he smiled. "You're wondering whether I think you'd do well there."

Smith, who rarely felt shy, could only nod.

"I don't know, and I'd be a fool to make a prediction. The wilderness is its own judge, and no others are trustworthy." A gleam appeared in Sir Walter's eyes. "There's only one way to find out, Captain."

"You're goading me."

"I suppose I am. That's because you've already made up your mind to go, although you may not know it."

It was Smith's turn to grin.

"Have you read my book, *The Discovery of Guiana?* I wrote it ten years ago, soon after I returned from the New World."

"I've tried to buy a copy, but none are available anywhere in London."

Raleigh became bitter. "Trust King James for that. He wants to destroy my work as well as me. Well, he can't. My book will still be read long after he's faded into one of the dark corners of history." He stood, went to a bookcase and returned with a slender, leather-bound volume. "Let me give you a copy. Read it, Captain, and absorb the lesson it teaches."

"I will, Sir Walter!"

"Some of my critics claimed I wrote fantasy. When you see the forests yourself, you'll realize I told the truth about them. The forces of Nature in America are as wild and primitive as the land itself. That's why men must work together and stand together. Personal differences are so petty, no matter what they might be, that they become absurd. Men must help each other— or everyone will perish. There's no alternative, no choice."

"I'll remember that."

Raleigh eyed him shrewdly. "I have an idea you will. Don't forget that men rarely enjoy cooperating with one another. They need to be disciplined, forced to work together for the common good. In our supposedly civilized lands, it's easy enough for everyone to strike out for himself. He becomes lost in the crowd, provided he doesn't go too far, and there are armies and constables to haul him back into line if he strays. There are even courts of law," he added wryly, "that condemn the innocent to imprisonment because kings become jealous and fear their popularity."

Smith felt a rush of sympathy for a great man who was being made to suffer unjustly.

"An expedition to the New World can succeed only if the leadership is strong and selfless. That's my legacy to you, Captain."

Smith stammered his thanks.

Sir Walter walked to the mesh-covered window and stared down at the ships in the Thames slowly making their way toward the open sea he loved. "When you first see the deep green of the New World forests, a deeper, purer green than any color you've ever known, think for a moment of me. When you eat your first American shellfish and bring down game more ferocious than any in this part of the world, think for a moment of me. The first time you crumble dried tobacco leaves, stuff them into a savage's clay pipe and smoke, think for a moment of me." His eyes became misty, and he cleared them, blinking a trifle angrily. "Perhaps, if you have time, you'll carve my name on a stone so that men will remember it was I who founded the land of Virginia."

"I'll do more than that, Sir Walter. I'll follow the advice you've given me, and if our venture succeeds, it will become a living tribute to you."

Raleigh continued to stand at the window, unmoving.

Smith couldn't be certain Sir Walter had heard him, but realized he had been dismissed.

The deputy warden was waiting for him at the entrance to the prison apartment and escorted him to the courtyard of the Tower. There he mounted his horse and rode out through the gates into the free world. In some mysterious way Sir Walter had helped him reach his final decision, and he thought that, perhaps, he had felt a need to carry on the work that Raleigh was now unable to perform.

Whatever his reasons, he was deliberately giving up the pleasant, comfortable future in England that he had earned in his years of fighting the battles of alien princes. He knew he would be subjecting himself to countless hazards and that, once committed, there could be no turning back. But he no longer cared. The lure of the unknown wilderness was too great.

III

THE FINANCIAL SPONSORS of the Virginia colony were blinded by greed, and most of the "gentlemen-adventurers" they appointed to the venture's ruling Council were weak, self-important and foolish. John Smith felt sick at heart after spending an afternoon with his new colleagues and the lords who were providing the funds for the great journey. The meeting had been held in the hall of the Earl of Southampton's town house, and Smith had been shocked by the cupidity of the shareholders.

His own financial interest was so small compared to that of the nobles that he had been given no voice in the proceedings, much to his dismay. What had disturbed him most was that Prince Henry and Archdeacon Hakluyt had stood alone in their hope of establishing a permanent, thriving colony in the New World. The others had paid polite lip service to the ideals expressed by the Prince of Wales, but had themselves repeatedly emphasized to the Council members that they wanted only to emulate the Spaniards who had been fortunate enough to find gold, emeralds and diamonds in other portions of the Americas.

Smith had been appointed to the Council, as he had anticipated, but had been stunned by the characters of his peers. The worst of them was Edward Maria Wingfield, a man who looked like a rustic clergyman but who put on airs. He had already proved himself stubborn, opinionated and short-sighted. George Kendal and Gabriel Archer were types Smith had known in his military service: they were both lazy blusterers who enjoyed giving orders but avoided doing any work themselves. John Ratcliffe, who would command the smallest of the three ships in the squadron, was a man with shifty eyes, an insincere smile and a manner so patently false that Smith instinctively distrusted him. Two of the other gentlemen-adventurers, George Percy, who was the younger brother of the Earl of Northumberland, and John Martin, seemed more substantial, but Smith had known their kind in military life, too. They were trustworthy enough, but could be easily led—or misled.

The Reverend Robert Hunt, the expedition's clergyman, was a pious friend of Archdeacon Hakluyt's, but seemed physically frail, and Smith privately wondered if he had the strength to endure the hardships that might lie ahead. Smith felt real confidence in only two men who were taking part in the enterprise. One was Bartholomew Gosnold, the veteran New World explorer, and the other was Christopher Newport, master of the largest of the vessels destined to make the voyage and commodore of the squadron.

Newport was an amiable, quiet-spoken giant in his late thirties, and it was obvious that he shared Smith's opinion of the sponsors and the other Council members. Again and again during the long meeting the eyes of the two men had met, and although they had exchanged no words, each knew the mind of the other.

Now, as the nobles and gentlemen-adventurers moved in solemn procession toward Whitehall, where they would be received in audience by King James, Smith and Newport sought one another's company and walked together. Smith smiled wryly as others jostled in order to find places for themselves nearer the front of the line, which was led by Prince Henry.

"Our first Atlantic gale," Newport said, "will send them scur-
rying to their beds. You've had experience at sea, Captain
Smith."

"Someone told you?"

"No, you've learned to balance yourself on a deck in a storm,
and it shows in your walk."

Smith grinned. "Well, you've been a soldier in your day,
Captain Newport. You carry your sword loose in its sheath,
ready to use, and you've learned the trick of carrying your pistols
on your hips, so you can reach them quickly when you must."

They looked at each other with mutual respect, and Newport
became thoughtful. "I've felt grave doubts about this venture,
but I'm more optimistic now. It may not be easy, but I believe
you and I, with God's help, may be able to organize a colony
that will endure."

It was immediately apparent to anyone who had visited the
Louvre in Paris and the Hofburg in Vienna that Whitehall was
an unpretentious palace. Its floors creaked, neither fireplaces nor
heavy drapes could keep out chilly drafts, and not even coats
of fresh gold-leaf paint on the walls could erase the impression
that it more closely resembled a merchant's house than a royal
residence.

King James I was responsible for the drab atmosphere. A
dour man with a long jaw and sad, tired eyes, he was an advo-
cate of frugality whose personal habits reflected his dislike of
parting with money. His informal audience chamber was lined
with benches, and the purple velvet cushions on his throne, the
only comfortable chair in the room, were badly faded. He wore
an inconspicuous suit of dark gray wool that made him look
drab in the presence of so many brilliantly dressed nobles, and

only his mammoth ruby ring, surrounded by a double circle of diamonds, indicated that he was one of the wealthiest men on earth.

He greeted the lords and Archdeacon Hakluyt absentmindedly as they came forward, one by one, to be recognized, and then, rather wearily, allowed Prince Henry to present the gentlemen-adventurers to him. When the brief ceremony was ended, he knew he was expected to make a few remarks, and after servants had distributed cups of punch, he offered a toast to the riches that would pour into the royal treasury from the New World.

John Smith and Christopher Newport looked at each other in alarm. If the King shared the view of so many associated with the expedition—that its primary purpose was to send precious metals and gems to England—the colony was doomed from the outset.

Prince Henry saw the glances, and immediately tried to repair the damage. "His Majesty," he said, speaking with greater confidence than he felt, "is looking forward to the permanent expansion of his realm. He is anticipating the day when Great Britain will become the greatest territorial power on earth."

The idea was pleasing to James, who brightened. "The Spaniards and the French," he said, "are expanding their empires very rapidly. Even the Dutch are acquiring new possessions. England must not be left behind in the race. We look to those brave men and their generous sponsors, who will make secure our hold on new lands."

Smith and Newport breathed inaudible sighs of relief. Now that the King had given his official sanction to the type of settlement they wanted to establish, there was at least a chance that the others could be persuaded to cooperate with them.

Ned Carson and Thaddeus Warner walked down the wharf
toward the waiting ships, their few personal possessions in the
sea bags of canvas they had slung over their shoulders. A biting
December wind ruffled the waters of the Thames, the vessels
strained at the lines that warped them to their berths, and the
boys made no secret of their fear. Like so many other youngsters
in England, where entire families were sometimes killed in frequently recurring plagues, both boys were orphans. The adventure in which they were participating was very dangerous, as
they well knew, but they had eagerly accepted the opportunity
to join the expedition. It was better to take risks and hope they
would improve their lot in the New World than to remain at
home, where sickness or starvation might kill them. They realized they might die on the high seas or in America, but the
exciting lure of the unknown was irresistible.

A final prayer service had been held, the last farewells to
friends and relatives had been said, and the great venture was
about to begin.

"The world will long remember December, 1606, as the
opening of a new page in human history," Archdeacon Hakluyt
had said in his sermon, but the boys found it difficult to recon-
cile his words with reality.

The ships that would carry the expedition across the Atlantic
looked almost absurdly puny, and the youngsters, who had
never been to sea, were convinced that a few giant waves could
smash the hulls to kindling. Christopher Newport's flagship,
the *Susan Constant,* was the largest craft in the squadron, but
had a gross weight of only one hundred tons. It was something
of a relief for the boys to know they were sailing on her, however, rather than on Captain Gosnold's forty-ton *God Speed*
or Captain Ratcliffe's tiny, twenty-ton pinnace *Discovery.*

The gentlemen-adventurers were gathered on the wharf, holding a conference of some sort, so Ned and Thaddeus stole past them and made their way across a narrow plank to the *Susan Constant.* Immediately they were in another world. A ship's mate directed them to stow their gear in a narrow, stuffy area below the main deck, which had a clearance of only four and one-half feet, and they were astonished to learn that they, together with more than fifty other settlers, would sleep in this cramped space on the whole, long voyage. Amidships on the main deck, fore of the mainmast, they saw an iron wood-burning stove set in a large tub of sand, and found that when weather permitted, their meals would be cooked there. When there were storms, snow or rain, they would eat cold food, mostly pickled beef or fish, and hard biscuits from which they were warned to tap the weevils.

A number of stout barrels were lashed to the deck, and some of the older settlers told the boys they contained the most precious of cargo, fresh water. Other kegs of water would be taken on board at the mouth of the Thames before the squadron put out to open sea.

Only Captain Newport enjoyed the privacy of his own cabin, but the gentlemen-adventurers were traveling in relative luxury. Captain Smith, Percy, Martin and the Reverend Hut were sharing a cabin near the master's quarters, and would eat their meals, read and talk in what was called the "great saloon." Thaddeus laughed when he saw the tiny cabin, which was about half the size of his family's small parlor. At least the ship's officers and the gentlemen-adventurers would enjoy the luxury of eating hot meals on the entire voyage, as their food would be cooked in an incredibly cramped indoor galley, which looked no larger than a clothes closet.

Sailors were busy rearranging the contents of the holds, dark
and forbidding caverns deep in the interior of the *Susan Constant*. There most of the supplies the colonists would need in the
New World were stored, the barrels of two cannon lashed to the
port and starboard bulkheads being the heaviest. In bags, boxes,
sacks and barrels were hundreds of items, goods that had been
painstakingly accumulated by Newport and Smith over a period
of many weeks. There were candles and tinderboxes and soft
soap, axes and cooking utensils, bolts of cloth and needles, barrels of the beer that every adult Englishman considered his
basic drink at meals, and a keg, sealed with wax to make it
waterproof, containing vegetable and grain seeds.

Smith, the boys heard, considered this keg the most valuable of all the supplies on board. They were also surprised to
find that one box contained scores of mirrors, which had been
purchased on the advice of Sir Walter Raleigh, who had said
that the savages of the New World were fascinated by these
simple objects in which they could see their own reflection.

The crews of the three ships, oblivious to the penetrating
cold, were moving up and down the rigging with the agility
of monkeys, and Ned nudged his friend when he saw that most
of the sailors were barefooted. "You'd think they'd freeze," he
said.

A grizzled seaman in a thick, short jacket and stocking cap
overheard the remark and laughed. "Lads," he said, "before this
voyage ends you'll be as hardened to the weather as any sea-
going man."

The boys looked at the figures moving aloft with such ease,
and marveled at the competence of men who felt no apprehen-
sion at such heights. But perhaps they, too, might someday over-
come their fear of the great ocean into which the tiny ships

would sail. Ned pulled up the collar of his greatcoat and shivered as he and his friend moved toward the rail.

Thaddeus stiffened and held a warning finger to his lips, and both boys edged closer to the gentlemen-adventurers, who were still standing on the wharf, apparently involved in a dispute.

Ratcliffe seemed to be wildly angry and was pointing an accusing finger at Smith, who was staring at him with cool disdain.

The expressions of several others in the group, Archer and Kendal in particular, indicated that they sympathized with Ratcliffe.

Only part of what Ratcliffe was saying could be heard on the deck, and it made no sense to the boys. "You're a meddler!" he shouted. "You've deliberately tried to hurt my good name."

Smith did not deign to reply.

Suddenly Ratcliffe started to draw his sword.

Before he could take it from its sheath, however, Smith whipped out his own blade, and his move was so rapid that Ned and Thaddeus were awed by his proficiency.

For an instant it seemed a sword fight would develop, but Christopher Newport quickly intervened. He stepped between the two principals and said something in an undertone to Smith, who shrugged and slipped his sword into its sheath. Ratcliffe was more difficult to handle, and Newport spoke to him at some length before he grudgingly put away his weapon, said something curtly to Smith over his shoulder and stomped off toward the pinnace.

The other gentlemen-adventurers continued to stand for a few moments, talking to each other in undertones, and then made their way to one or another of the three ships.

The boys hurried off down the deck of the *Susan Constant*

as the Council members came on board. The last to cross the gangplank were Smith and Newport, and the ship's master was piped aboard by the bo's'n's mate. As the high-pitched sound cleared away, Ned and Thaddeus could hear Smith talking to the expedition's commodore.

"If it's true that Ratcliffe has a criminal record under another name," John Smith said, "this is the first I've heard of it. And in my opinion that's his business. I care only about a man's present character, not his background."

"I feel sure," Newport replied soothingly, "that a man of your caliber wouldn't repeat stories about anyone, regardless of whether they're true or false. Dismiss the matter from your mind."

The boys forgot the dispute in the excitement of the final preparations. Ships' officers shouted orders, sails were unfurled, the lines were cast off and the anchors weighed. Then, slowly, the little squadron edged out into the Thames and started downstream, the *Susan Constant* in the lead, Gosnold's *God Speed* close behind and Ratcliffe's *Discovery* bringing up the rear.

The sails filled, and Ned and Thaddeus took their final fill of familiar London on their right, Southwark on their left. Others in the expedition were lining the rail, too, the gentlemen-adventurers standing near the prow. Captain Newport was on his quarterdeck, supervising the operation, and at his command a set of small, colored signal flags were run up to the *Susan Constant*'s top-gallants.

The other ships soon responded with signals of their own, and the boys watched in silence as the seamen cheered. Finally Ned summoned the courage to tap a sailor on the arm. "What does the message say, please?"

"May God grant us a calm crossing and a safe landing."

When London faded from sight, the Reverend Hunt summoned the entire company of the *Susan Constant,* passengers and crew members alike, to a short prayer service on the chilly, open deck. And everyone repeated the words he read from the Book of Psalms: *"Preserve me, O God: for in thee do I put my trust."*

The open countryside of rural England stretched out on both sides of the river, and the boys left the open deck to begin their duties, serving the officers and gentlemen-adventurers. It did not occur to either Ned or Thaddeus that a dark cloud had already formed and was hovering over the expedition. The scene they had witnessed on the wharf was the opening act of a tragedy that would create still deeper misunderstanding and, in time, would cause suffering—and disaster.

Newport's squadron put into port at the thriving town of Blackwall, on the north bank of the River Thames, before sailing into the English Channel and, beyond it, the Atlantic Ocean. At Blackwall, final preparations were made for the great adventure. As many casks of fresh water as the three ships could comfortably carry were hauled aboard and lashed to the decks. The last provisions were purchased, including fresh beef, unsalted butter, newly laid eggs and sweet milk.

"Enjoy these luxuries while you may," the sailors told the passengers. "You won't taste their likes again for a long time."

Ned and Thaddeus, who were already growing familiar with the stores carried on the voyage, ate heartily. They knew that soon they would live only on pickled beef, salt fish, bacon and salt pork, with occasional dishes of rice, raisins, prunes and currants. They would have oatmeal and hard biscuits for breakfast and occasionally, for supper, would eat roasted mutton that had been minced and was being preserved in oil. Desserts would be few. The ships carried large quantities of cheese, and there were sacks of sugar among the provisions, too, but inasmuch as cooking facilities were limited, no cakes would be baked.

In all, there were now one hundred and fifty passengers, about twenty having joined the company at Blackwall. These men came from every walk of life. Among the gentlemen-adventurers, Percy had done no work of any kind in his twenty-two years. John Smith was the most experienced, and both Archer and Kendal claimed to have been soldiers. The "commoners" who made up the bulk of the company came from many walks of life. Leading the list was the surgeon, who, after the custom of the seventeenth century, was also the barber.

There were stonemasons and bricklayers, a blacksmith, two tailors and several carpenters. The vast majority had worked as common laborers and had no special skills of any kind. Ned overheard Captain Smith remarking to Newport that he was concerned because literally none had ever earned their living as either farmers or soldiers, two occupations that both believed essential for the survival of the colony.

The gentlemen-adventurers were the only members of the expedition allowed ashore at Blackwall. They went into the town from all three vessels for the forty-eight hours that the squadron remained in port. There, in a waterfront inn, Ratcliffe renewed his quarrel with Smith, and although the gentlemen tried to keep the matter quiet, the entire company soon learned the details.

Ratcliffe, it appeared, had once served a term of five years in Newgate Prison, London's most notorious penitentiary, after being convicted as a forger and embezzler. At that time he had used the name of John Sickelmore. Someone had learned of his past, and had informed the other gentlemen-adventurers of it. Ratcliffe had accused Smith of deliberately trying to injure him, and because Smith refused to defend himself, believing the charges beneath contempt, the others were strongly inclined to believe Ratcliffe.

Thaddeus and Ned knew that Newport was certain Smith had said nothing, and the boys privately suspected that the overbearing Kendal was the man who had spread the story. When the gentlemen-adventurers from all three ships gathered in the great saloon of the *Susan Constant* to discuss the subject, the two boys, bringing them food and drink, noticed that Kendal often smiled slyly to himself and fanned the flames of the others' indignation.

The upshot of the childish matter was that Smith was shunned by most of his colleagues, and a genuine rift developed between him and his peers.

Newport tried to heal the breach, saying repeatedly that no one really cared about Ratcliffe's past, that Smith stood to gain nothing by bringing it up and that the whole expedition would be the poorer if there were hard feelings among the leaders. But Archer and Kendal refused to drop the subject, Radcliffe remained indignant, and Wingfield, who had already indicated he hoped to be elected President of the Council after the company landed in the New World, was heard to say that he considered Smith unfit for Council membership.

"This is ridiculous," Smith said to Newport, the one man in whom he confided. "Let's assume that I did spread the story—which you and I know I didn't. It seems to me that I'm being punished because another man was foolish in his youth and was sent to prison. It doesn't make sense."

Newport hoped that the long voyage would give tempers time to cool and would clear the air.

Meanwhile, when all hands were piped aboard the ships just prior to sailing from Blackwall, Ned and Thaddeus were aware of a distinct coolness toward Smith on the part of the other gentlemen-adventurers who were traveling on the *Susan Constant*. Percy and Martin seemed uneasy in Captain Smith's presence, and even Reverend Martin showed a distinct embarrassment.

Their attitude made Smith so uncomfortable that he offered his services to Newport, and he was accepted as a temporary ship's officer. As acting first mate of the *Susan Constant* it was his duty to give the orders that would set the squadron in motion. Two hours before dawn on the morning of December 19, 1606, he came up to the quarterdeck, made sure all was in readiness there, and then quickly inspected the vessel.

Captain Gosnold, on the *God Speed,* called to him that he was ready to sail, too.

Ratcliffe, on the *Discovery,* wanted nothing to do with Smith, and resented the sudden emergence into a responsible naval post of the man he considered his deadly enemy. He had no real choice, however, and in a surly voice he shouted that his ship was ready, too.

"Tell the commodore," Smith said to Ned, who had been summoned to the quarterdeck to carry messages, "that the squadron is prepared for sea duty."

"Yes, sir." The boy ran to the master's cabin, where Newport was studying his charts of the Atlantic by the light of a small oil lamp.

Newport came up to the quarterdeck at once, and Smith greeted him with a salute and a broad grin. "We're ready to cast off, sir."

"Cast off and weigh anchors!" Newport called, and the blare of a trumpet told the small crowd huddled on the shore in the early morning cold that the great advanture was about to begin.

Wheels turned, chains clanked, and the anchors of the three ships were slowly hauled up.

"You may set sail, Captain Smith!" Newport stood erect, and his resonant voice was firm.

"Set sails," Smith commanded. "Helmsman, steer a course south by southwest."

"Very good, sir."

The *Susan Constant* drifted out into the estuary of the Thames, her sails filling slowly, and headed toward the choppy waters of the English Channel. The *God Speed,* under Gosnold's brilliant handling, moved gracefully in the larger ship's wake. Ratcliffe, bringing up the rear of the column, was somewhat more erratic, but both Newport and Smith charitably conceded that a pinnace of only twenty tons did not ride easily in rough seas.

The little crowd on the shore sent up a thin, ragged cheer, and a flock of seagulls swooped low over the stern of the *Susan Constant,* then rose higher into the air, intending to follow the squadron into open waters.

The first rays of light streaked an ominously dark sky, and it finally lightened to a dull, overcast gray. A sharp, icy wind howled through the rigging, and the flagship began to roll and pitch as she headed into the Channel.

All of the settlers were crowding the decks of the ships, and some of them peered intently toward the fast-receding shore. A few of the younger men smiled, and one or two tried to joke, but the majority of the colonists were silent and solemn. The same thought was in every mind, but no one voiced aloud the universal question: "Will we ever see England again?"

By Christmas Day, 1606, the three ships were in the open Atlantic, plowing through heavy seas toward an unknown, unexplored continent. By now most of the colonists were beginning to lose their fear of the rough, gray waters, and had become accustomed to the constant, erratic motion of the tiny vessels. With exceptional good fortune, they had been told, they might reach the New World in six weeks. But if they encountered consistently bad weather, which was normal in winter, the voyage might take as long as three months.

Ned and Thaddeus were kept busy serving meals and attending to the other wants of Newport, his officers and the gentlemen-adventurers, but the older passengers had literally nothing to do. They had no desire to remain in their incredibly cramped sleeping quarters, yet there was virtually nowhere else to go. Some braved the open deck, walking up and down for exercise, and were drenched by freezing saltwater spray. The few who knew how to read borrowed Bibles from Newport and Smith, and haltingly tried to read aloud to their companions in order to help pass the time. When the Reverend Hunt heard of their plight, he read two hours each day from Scriptures to the assembled colonists, a practice he kept up throughout the long voyage.

The passengers slept for hours at a time, told each other tall stories—and speculated on the life that awaited them. But none had a clear idea of what really awaited them in the land of the limitless forests, and they succeeded only in frightening themselves with their tales of the cannibals and fire-breathing monsters they expected to find in the American wilderness.

John Smith was too busy in his work as a ship's officer to pay much attention to the snubs of his fellow leaders. And Newport, still hoping the senseless display of anger toward an innocent man would peter out, continued to urge Smith to avoid arguments with the other gentlemen-adventurers.

On Christmas Day the Reverend Hunt held a special service in the great saloon of the *Susan Constant,* reading the story of the Nativity from the Book of Luke. The cabin was so crowded that some of the passengers and seamen were unable to find places, so he held a second worship service immediately following the first. The men and boys sang some of the old Christmas hymns that had been traditional in England since the Middle Ages, and some of the singers felt so homesick they wept without shame.

Then a special, surprise treat awaited the whole company, on board all three vessels. Just before sailing from Blackwall Captain Newport had distributed freshly slaughtered geese to the cooks, having paid for the birds out of his own pocket, and now everyone dined on roasted stuffed goose, just as people were doing back in England. John Smith, who had shared Newport's secret, had purchased enough plum puddings to serve the whole company, and the settlers, sailors and ship's officers ate heartily.

It was the last pleasant meal they were destined to enjoy for a long time. On the day after Christmas the first of a series of fierce gales howled out of the west, and the little ships bobbed helplessly in the Atlantic like corks. Some of the colonists were ill, and others were so terrified they stayed on their knees, praying. The masters of the ships had themselves lashed to their quarterdecks so they wouldn't be washed overboard, and thanks to the superb seamanship of Newport, assisted by Smith, the squadron managed to ride out the storm.

When the wind and sea subsided, it was discovered that deck rails had been smashed, a giant wave had damaged the prow of the *God Speed,* requiring the immediate attentions of carpenters, and ripped sails on all three ships had to be replaced.

The passengers, allowed in the open again, marveled at calm, blue-green seas sparkling in bright winter sunlight. Some believed a miracle had occurred, and that they had been saved by Divine Providence. Experienced hands smiled politely and, at Newport's orders, kept silent. A great many miracles would be needed if the expedition hoped to reach the New World without suffering further damage.

IV

"NEVER IN A LIFE AT SEA," Christopher Newport wrote in his logbook on February 23, 1607, "have I seen or felt a more horrendous storm than that which held us in its thrall for four nights and three days, and which, thanks to the merciful intervention of the Almighty, finally blew away at dawn this morning."

Later generations would call a storm of such ferocious intensity a hurricane. Giant waves towered over the little ships, then crashed down on them, and the winds were so wild that sails became useless and tillers unmanageable. The masters of the ships concentrated on trying to stay afloat. Several barrels and boxes stored in the hold of the *God Speed* broke loose, and as it was too dangerous for sailors to even try to lash them down again, Captain Gosnold could do nothing to salvage that portion of his cargo. The wood splintered, then smashed, and the contents were ruined.

On the second day of the storm the *Discovery* vanished and was feared lost. No one on the other two ships actually saw the little pinnace founder, however, and everyone continued to hope she would ride out the gale. On the morning of the third day disaster struck the *Susan Constant*. A particularly vicious wave broke her foremast half-through, and the upper portion fell into the raging sea. It as still attached to its base, however, and by dragging in the water acted as a crude anchor.

The ship, buffeted by waves and wind, was unable to move freely, and spun about, turning first to starboard, then to port, as waves crashed into her. It soon became evident that the ship would break up unless she was relieved, but anyone who tried to make his way forward across the wind-swept, foaming deck would be inviting suicide. It was equally plain, however, that if no one volunteered, the entire *Susan Constant* company would perish. John Smith elected to take the gamble and prepared for his battle with the elements quietly. Although regarded as flamboyantly theatrical by many, he was a man who actually avoided dramatics when taking grave risks. As George Percy wrote, many years later, his achievements were spectacular, but his manner of performing them was modest.

First he tied a long rope to the mainmast, fastening the other end around his own waist. If he should be washed overboard, there was at least an outside chance that others could haul him back onto the deck of the ship before he was drowned. Then he looped a strong leather thong around his right wrist, attaching the other end to the handle of an ax.

Captain Newport was reluctant to see him go off to almost certain death, and urged him to wait a short time in the hope that the storm would subside somewhat. But, even though the commodore, himself lashed to the rail of the quarterdeck, shouted loudly, he could not make himself heard above the shrieking of the wind and crashing of the waves against the battered hull of the flagship. Some of the colonists, Ned and Thaddeus among them, crowded to the few rain-streaked windows that looked out on the deck.

Smith started to move forward slowly, lurching and stumbling, yet somehow managing to regain his balance and stay on his feet. Already drenched by the cold rain and icy sea water, his hands and feet felt numb, but through sheer force of will he was able to coordinate his movements. Slowly, inch by inch and foot by foot, he edged forward, half-blinded by the spray and rain, his face and hands stinging.

The *Susan Constant* heaved erratically, swooping down into the trough between waves, then starting to rise on another swell before being battered fore and aft, on port and starboard, by a succession of new waves as she swung to and fro crazily. Suddenly a high, solid wall of water smashed down on the helpless vessel, engulfing her and knocking Smith off his feet.

He went under, and was powerless to save himself as the rush of the wave carried him like a toy along the length of the deck. Half-drowned, he called on his last reserves of strength and groped for something to which he could cling. "The Almighty was good to me, and to my companions," he wrote in later years. "I felt my left arm graze against something solid, and, by now scarcely aware of what I was doing, reached for it with both hands. Nearly dead, I still retained just enough presence of mind to know that, if my effort failed, I would soon be lost. Thanks to the Lord, my stiff fingers closed around a portion of the main deck railing that had not yet been destroyed."

The wave rolled on, but Smith remained behind, gasping for air, sputtering, and so weakened that for a few moments he had no idea what had happened to him. But a sixth sense quickly alerted him to the dangers of his situation, and all at once, as his vision cleared and his mind began to function again, he realized that the wave had actually helped him. It had carried him forward toward his goal, and he was only a few feet from the base of the broken mast.

He staggered toward it, clutched it and held on tightly as another giant wave rolled across the deck. In fact, his grasp was so tight that for many days thereafter he found splinters embedded in the flesh of his palms and fingers.

Realizing that no man could long survive such a merciless battering, he hauled himself to his feet as soon as the wave had gone on. First, as an extra precaution, he looped a length of his line around the base of the mast, and then he started to work. He knew his strength was partly depleted, and that if he tried to do too much too fast he might be defeating himself. Yet, at the same time, he realized that every moment's delay increased the danger to everyone on board the ship. Speed took priority over safety, and planting his feet wide apart, he began to hack at the broken mast.

The ax rose and fell, cutting into the waterlogged wood, and each blow was an agony that drained him. His shoulders and arms felt as heavy as solid metal, his legs and thighs ached, and he found it impossible to stop his knees from quivering. But his exertions had at least one beneficial effect, warming him so that he no longer felt frozen.

Twice he was forced to halt his efforts as new waves crashed down on the *Susan Constant,* and he hugged the base of the mast, swallowing vast quantities of water before he was able to pull himself to his feet again. The work seemed to last an eternity, and he was later surprised to learn that it actually took no more than a quarter of an hour. The ax slashed again and again through the soggy wood, and finally the mast came free.

Suddenly a new danger arose. Another wave loomed overhead, and Smith felt deep fear. The freed mast was still lying in part on the deck, and it appeared from the angle of the wave that the water would send the tall pole, made heavier by the water, directly onto him, crushing him.

There was literally nothing he could do to protect himself, and he prayed silently as he clutched the stump of the mast. The wave unleashed its fury, tons of water poured across the bow of the ship, and Smith was knocked to the deck. When he finally recovered, dazed but grateful that he was still alive, the broken mast was gone. The sea had spared him and, miraculously, had carried away the sail-fouled pole that had been acting as an anchor. At last the *Susan Constant* was free.

His mission completed, Smith removed the loop in his line from the stump and began his perilous walk toward the quarterdeck. He was so feeble now that he felt certain he could not reach his destination, but he failed to take into account the resourcefulness of Christopher Newport. The commodore, realizing that Smith's strength had given out, pulled on the line, with the assistance of two sailors.

Smith was no longer able to stand erect, and dropped to his hands and knees. For the better part of the distance he crawled toward safety, partly under his own power, in part thanks to the pressure being exerted at the other end of the rope.

When he finally reached the quarterdeck he appeared

stunned, and at Newport's orders the two sailors took him down to the cabins. The task of opening a hatch in the face of a hurricane wind was monumental, but at last they succeeded, and eager hands helped Smith to reach the warmth of the ship's interior. In spite of his exhaustion his pride was still great, and he refused to allow anyone to help him change into dry clothes. As a special concession he permitted Ned to get various belongings from his sea chest; then he closed the door of his cabin and dressed.

When he emerged the cook was waiting for him with a mug of steaming broth, which revived him, and he was surprised to discover that the passengers and crew alike regarded him as a hero. Only the other gentlemen-adventurers refused to admit that he had saved the ship from certain disaster; they claimed he had been showing off in order to win greater popularity. His own view was, simply, that he done something that had been urgently necessary.

The *Susan Constant* was no longer crippled and was able to ride out the storm. Winds and high seas continued to batter her, but she had regained her buoyant mobility. Under the superb handling of Newport, who did not leave his quarterdeck until the weather showed distinct improvement, the ship rode out the hurricane.

The *God Speed* also managed to remain afloat and suffered relatively little damage. Bartholomew Gosnold proved himself a ship's master worthy of the name. But, when the skies cleared, the wind subsided and the sea became tranquil, there was still no sign of the *Discovery*.

The members of Newport's crew went to work with a vengeance. A new foremast was hoisted into place and jury-rigged; carpenters repaired the damage to the flagship's bow and, taking full advantage of the unexpectedly good weather, also put up a new rail.

The two vessels continued on their course, and twenty-four hours later the lookout in the crow's nest of the *Susan Constant* sighted something in the distance. "Sail ho!" he shouted, and the officers and seamen raced to their stations.

It was known that many pirate vessels roamed the Atlantic, and both Newport and Gosnold prepared for the worst, dragging up their small cannon and waiting for an assault. To their astonishment, however, the lines of the little ship that approached them seemed familiar, and at last they recognized the *Discovery.* Ratcliffe, they were to learn, had been blown off his course and had been completely at the mercy of the storm. Those on board the tiny pinnace were surprised and grateful to be alive, and everyone, on all three ships, was astonished that the *Discovery* and the other vessels should have been able to rejoin forces in the vast expanses of the Atlantic. "The Lord, in His infinite wisdom, has insured that we travel together," the Reverend Hunt said, and no one was able to disagree.

Carpenters were sent across smooth waters to the *Discovery* in the captains' gigs, or small boats, from the other two ships, and after a hard day's labor the pinnace was made seaworthy again. The voyage was resumed.

Then the weather became capricious. The prevailing winds in the Atlantic normally blew from west to east, but the winter of 1606–7 proved an exception. The ships' masters discovered they were being blown toward the southwest, and Newport finally accepted his destiny. Rather than try to stay in the North Atlantic, as he had planned, he decided to stop fighting the winds, and signaled to the other ships that they would let the winds carry them to the West Indian Islands.

Gradually, almost imperceptibly, the weather became warmer. The colonists, heartily sick of their long cold weeks at sea, were able to enjoy walking and sunning themselves on the decks of the ships and were eagerly looking forward to a visit ashore. On the morning of March 24, 1607, land was sighted, and that afternoon the ships dropped anchor off the West Indian island of Dominica, which had first been discovered by Christopher Columbus in 1493.

Everyone went ashore, and the colonists saw their first American Indians, members of the Carib tribe, who were short, swarthy and exceptionally friendly. Some of the passengers and crew members were eager to trade with the savages, but Newport gave strict orders that he alone would barter with them. He did, exchanging knives and copper beads, mirrors and axes for quantities of wild boar, seagulls' eggs and a variety of tropical fruits unlike any food the men had ever before eaten. A feast was held, and then most of the company went swimming, racing into the warm water from the black, volcanic beach of Dominica. Ned and Thaddeus, grimy after spending three months at sea without baths, thoroughly enjoyed themselves. But an even greater luxury was that of drinking fresh water from a swiftly flowing brook that ran down from the mountain heights dominating the island.

The expedition spent two days at Dominica. Dirty clothes were washed, casks were refilled with pure, sweet water, and everyone gorged on the strange fruits of the island. Then the company spent a number of days making a leisurely tour of the West Indies. On March 27 they landed on the island of Guadeloupe, where they found a natural spring so hot that, after several of the gentlemen-adventurers had shot some wild boar, they amused themselves by boiling pork in the spring. A few days later the ships dropped anchor at the little island of Nevis.

Appetites had been whetted for fresh meat, so Newport led the entire expedition inland. The majority of the men were armed with muskets, pistols or fowling pieces, but they found no game. Instead they discovered some pleasant mineral springs, and spent an entire afternoon bathing. The spirits of the colonists and sailors were gradually being restored after the grueling voyage, and Newport wisely decided to spend several days at Nevis.

Hunting parties kept the company supplied with rabbits and birds, unlike any that had ever been seen by Englishmen, which proved to be succulent when roasted. Others went fishing and discovered the joys of eating swordfish, which was in time to become a staple item in the diet of North Americans. There was an unexpected drama that enthralled Thaddeus and Ned, too. The boys accompanied a fishing party that went out in one of the gigs, and saw a vicious fight between a swordfish and a thresher whale. Both of the participants were mortally wounded, and everyone who witnessed the duel was struck by the realization that primitive, cruel barbarism was commonplace in the raw wilderness of the New World.

On April 4 the company went ashore on one of the Virgin Islands, where pleasures were mixed with disappointment. Although the jungles were lush, and colorful but odorless flowers grew in profusion, no fresh water was found for either drinking or bathing. Several tortoises were caught, however, and were so large their meat supplied the entire band with enough food for three days. The fishing parties continued to enjoy good fortune, and some of the gentlemen-adventurers became convinced that the sea would continue to provide them with all the food they needed after they moved father north. Only Newport,

Gosnold and Smith reserved their opinions and refused to accept the optimistic forecasts of the others.

During the visit to the Virgin Islands the explosive hatred of Ratcliffe, Archer and Kendal for Smith finally came to a head. The ship's officers and gentlemen-adventurers from all three vessels had been spending virtually all of their time together since arriving in the West Indian Islands, and it was inevitable, perhaps, that the simmering feud should have boiled to a climax.

Smith's curiosity provided the spark. One day he captured a giant lizard, more than five feet long, subsequently known as an iguana, which he described as bearing a resemblance to a crocodile. Most of his colleagues were superstitious, half-educated men, and spurred by Ratcliffe and Kendal, they reached the absurd conclusion, which to them was logical, that Smith possessed magical powers and had in some inexplicable, mysterious way, transformed an innocent creature of the tropics into a man-devouring, fire-breathing dragon.

The early seventeenth century was a period in which people everywhere believed in the power exerted by witches and their male counterparts, warlocks. Hysteria was common in England, where those with so-called supernatural talents were sometimes solemnly tried in courts of justice and occasionally burned at the stake. Therefore it wasn't difficult, thousands of miles from home, when men were still recuperating from the terrors of a wild sea voyage, to arouse the feelings of already prejudiced men against Captain John Smith.

Ratcliffe initiated the outcry and was subtly helped by Kendal, who was probably doing everything in his power to prevent anyone from learning that he himself had been the original mischief-maker. The ambitious, incompetent Wingfield, who saw Smith as his primary rival, was easy to convince, and although Martin and Percy later said they had not really believed Smith was an evil sorcerer, they went along with the majority.

Gabriel Archer proposed that Smith be hanged from the nearest tree, and that the sentence be carried out at once.

Christopher Newport and Bartholomew Gosnold protested, but no one listened to them. And the Reverend Hunt, who preached against Satan every week of his life, didn't quite know where to stand.

The gentlemen-adventurers approached Smith in a body as he was taking a nap in the shade of a banyan tree, Newport and Gosnold still arguing with the majority.

The instinct that had enabled John Smith to survive unscathed in the war against the Turks helped him again. He awakened suddenly, sat upright, and when he saw the heavy rope Archer and Kendal were carrying, he knew at once what his peers were planning. He snatched one of his pistols from the ground beside him, whipped his sword from its sheath and sprang to his feet.

His assailants paused, with good reason. They knew he was a fine swordsman and an expert shot, and under the circumstances would not hesitate to attack anyone who came too close.

Archer's hand crept toward his own pistol, but at Smith's sharp command he raised both hands high above his head. No one else dared to move.

Wingfield, speaking in a loud voice, ordered Smith to lay down his arms and surrender.

Many of the commoners heard the booming tone and hurried to the scene. Ned and Thaddeus, who had been investigating the wonders of the "traveler's palm," a tree that spouted potable water when tapped, were among those who ran through the jungle. Men and boys alike were stunned by what they saw, and stood still, too shocked to speak.

Then Wingfield, spurred by the presence of an audience, repeated his order.

With one accord the colonists took up places behind Smith. They already regarded him as their natural leader, and did not hesitate to make their feelings clear. But he was anxious to protect them from vindictiveness or possible injury and, quietly thanking them for their support, asked them to move aside. Then, in the same calm tone, he told the gentlemen-adventurers he would kill the first to raise a hand against him.

They knew he was not bluffing, and were afraid to rush him, but at the same time didn't want to lose stature by backing down.

Christopher Newport saw his opportunity to intervene as a peacemaker. The charges against Smith were unsupported by factual evidence, he declared, and therefore should be dropped. Even if some of the gentlemen-adventurers were still convinced that Smith was a sorcerer, the services he had rendered the entire company during the hurricane at sea should earn him a full pardon.

Grudgingly, with no real alternative, Wingfield, Archer and Kendal agreed. The incident came to an abrupt close.

But its repercussions were lasting. Smith naturally resented the totally unjustified attempt to rob him of his life and thereafter carried his pistols and sword at all times. He never trusted any of his colleagues except Newport and Gosnold, even though he had to work closely with them. The lack of trust was mutual. They considered him an outsider, never took him into their confidence, and availed themselves of his superior talents only when forced by circumstances beyond their control to appeal to him for help. The senseless dispute, now blown far out of proportion to the misunderstanding that had sparked it, would cost the colony dearly in the following year.

For the immediate present, however, a surface calm had been restored, and Newport decided to set sail at once in order to keep the company occupied. On April 6 the squadron put in at the little island of Mona, near Puerto Rico, and while the sailors again refilled the water casks, the commodore marched everyone else inland through the jungle. Several wild boars were killed and a few fruits were collected, but the intense tropical heat caused considerable suffering. Edward Brookes, a gentleman-adventurer who neither held nor wanted a Council seat, and who was friendly with everyone, after the manner of portly men, suddenly collapsed on the trail. Before those nearest to him in the line could come to his assistance, he was dead.

That same night he was buried on the heights above Mona's main beach, the first member of the expedition to die. A stone, on which his name and the date were carved by a stonemason, was placed at the head of his grave, as was a crude cross. The Reverend Hunt conducted a brief service, and then the entire company, much sobered, returned to the ships.

On April 9 a landing was made at the rocky little island of Moneta, the men going ashore in the ships' boats. There they found wildfowl of every kind in profusion. As Smith later wrote, "They flew over our heads as thick as drops of hail. Besides, they made such a noise that we were not able to hear one another speak. Furthermore, we were not able to set our feet on the ground, but either on fowls or eggs which lay so thick in the grass."

The men were quick to take advantage of the opportunity that had so unexpectedly been afforded them. Two boats laden with wild ducks and other birds were rowed back to the ships, and two others were filled with eggs. This food, combined with the fish that were being caught in large numbers from the decks, gave everyone more than enough to eat. All meals were being cooked and eaten in the open, and the colonists, putting the tragedy of Brookes' death out of their minds, believed they had found an earthly paradise.

Newport, Gosnold and Smith conferred privately, however, and reached the joint conclusion that the expedition should leave the tropics and sail for Virginia. None of them knew any-thing about weather conditions in the land of their destina-tion, and, as Smith said, it was imperative that they plant their spring crops, build their houses and prepare for a possibly harsh winter ahead. None of the other leaders appointed by London, it appeared, was thinking beyond the pleasures of the immediate present.

Newport did not bother to consult them, and on April 10, at dawn, he ordered the squadron to weigh anchors and set sail for the north. Not until later that morning did most members of the expedition realize they were traveling on the last leg of their momentous journey.

Fish were still plentiful, and anyone throwing a line over-board was almost certain to land something edible. But the company had eaten so much fish by now that the catches were thrown back into the sea. Captain Smith urged that quantities of fish be preserved in salt or brine for future use, but his ad-vice was ignored, to the expedition's later sorrow.

On April 14 the squadron crossed the Tropic of Cancer and sailed into temperate waters. Seven days later, while off the coast of what were to become the Carolinas, but out of sight of land, the ships were struck by a sudden gale that blew them northward off their course. No serious damage was sustained, but on the morning of April 22, when the seas were calm again,

Newport summoned the masters of the *God Speed* and the *Discovery* to a private meeting on board the *Susan Constant*.

There, with John Smith the only other person present, the commodore admitted that he was lost. It was his mariner's hunch that the ships should continue to sail northward, and as neither Gosnold nor Ratcliffe had any better suggestions, they agreed.

For the next seventy-two hours all three ships took frequent soundings, but at no time did they find themselves in waters of less depth than three hundred fathoms. Most of the charts in Newport's possession were hazy and inaccurate, and as no one had ever accurately mapped that section of the Atlantic, they thought it possible they had completely missed the North American continent and were sailing in unknown seas.

Captain Ratcliffe became panicky, and on April 25 proposed that the plan to establish a colony be abandoned and that, instead, all three ships sail directly back to England.

Newport firmly rejected the suggestion, and was supported by Gosnold. Smith, who had no voice in the decision, was secretly relieved.

At daybreak on April 26, the lookout in the crow's nest of the *Susan Constant* called, "Land ho!"

Passengers raced to the deck in such large numbers that they interfered with the efficient operation of the ship, and Newport was forced to order them below again. Through his glass he was able to make out a smudge of a green darker than the blue-green of the sea, and immediately ordered the squadron to proceed westward.

By noon the smudge had broadened and had become a long, green line on the horizon. Late that afternoon the great forests of the New World were plainly visible, and the colonists, now

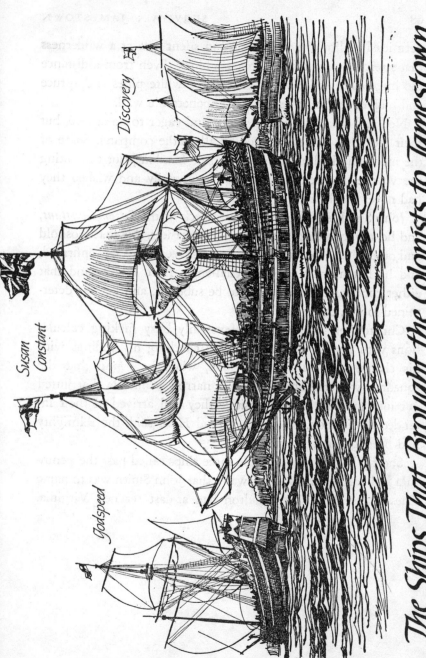

Godspeed

Susan Constant

Discovery

The Ships That Brought the Colonists to Jamestown

permitted to line the rails, stared in silent awe at a wilderness that stretched out as far as they could see. Even from a distance the huge oaks and elms, the towering white pines and spruce and maples formed a seemingly impenetrable wall.

Ned and Thaddeus were excited and eager to go ashore, but their feelings were not shared by all of the company. Some of the men, who had not traveled outside London prior to making the voyage, glanced an one another uneasily and wished they had never left home.

John Smith stood on the quarterdeck of the *Susan Constant,* and he, too, contemplated the raw wilderness. All that Gosnold and others had told him about America seemed to be confirmed, and he felt a fresh sense of challenge. Here was a land that either conquered man or had to be subdued, and he was determined to win the great duel.

Christopher Newport was feverishly busy making calculations with his few instruments and checking his findings with his charts. Late in the afternoon, when he found that the squadron was standing off a long, narrow peninsula that jutted out into the sea, he was positive they had arrived at their intended destination. As the Reverend Hunt said, the Almighty had been guiding them.

Shortly before sundown the three ships sailed past the peninsula and entered the body of water that John Smith was to name Chesapeake Bay. The squadron had at last reached Virginia.

V

IT WAS SO LATE in the day on April 26, 1607, that no real attempt to explore the immediate area near the anchored ships could be made. And common sense dictated that it would be unwise for the entire company to go ashore and brave unknown wilderness perils when night would descend at any time. It was important to know something about the region, however, so a party of twenty-three went off in the ships' boats and had the honor of being the first Englishmen to land.

The Reverend Hunt was one member of the group, and as soon as he stepped ashore he scooped up a handful of earth. Asking the others to bow their heads in prayer, he asked God's blessing. It was customary for clergymen of the time to deliver long sermons and make equally long intercessions with the Almighty, and the Reverend Hunt was no exception. Daylight was fading, the forest looked forbidding, and the others became increasingly nervous as he continued to pray. Eventually the always-practical John Smith reminded him, with a cough, that the purpose of the trip ashore had not been just that of conducting a worship service.

Archer, Wingfield and Percy were among the gentlemen-adventurers in the group, but all three were reluctant to plunge into the dark forest, so Smith took the lead. Half of the party followed him, and Percy, ashamed of his weakness, went with them, but Archer and Wingfield elected to remain close to the shore, in sight of the ships.

Little could be learned in a brief inspection, but Smith and his companions found the trees majestic. All that Gosnold and Sir Walter Raleigh had said about the beauty of the forest appeared to be true. The soil was black and promised to be excellent for planting when the ground was cleared. And the men discovered several rapidly flowing, sweet-water brooks that emptied into the bay. When the party returned to the *Susan Constant,* it was agreed that Virginia was a hospitable land and that the possibilities of establishing the colony in the immediate vicinity were bright.

That night, after everyone had eaten and the excited settlers were still on the decks of the ships, someone noticed that two long canoes of birchbark, filled with half-naked savages, had put out from the mainland. Most of the gentlemen-adventurers were ready to give the Indians a warm welcome, but Smith and Newport were more cautious, observing that the warriors carried bows in their mouths and quivers of arrows over their shoulders.

The braves quickly demonstrated that their intentions were hostile. When their war canoes were about twenty-five or thirty yards from the *Susan Constant,* they sent a shower of arrows at the strangers. Gabriel Archer suffered two minor flesh wounds, and a sailor named Matthew Morton, who achieved renown in his own right some years later when he made voyages of discovery to South America and the East Indies, sustained a somewhat more severe injury.

Smith and Newport reacted instantly. Drawing the pistols they habitually carried, they fired at the warriors. It was too dark to determine whether they hit their foes, but the sound of the pistol fire frightened the savages, who paddled ashore and vanished into the forest.

Early on the morning of April 27 the gentlemen-adventurers and ships' captains held a meeting, and Wingfield, who had been working for the support of the others, was elected President of the Council, or Governor. The colonists, who neither liked nor trusted him, were deeply disappointed that the post had not gone to Smith. But there had been literally no chance he would be elected, even though he was the one member of the Council who had demonstrated qualities of leadership. His peers, jealous of his talents and envious of his popularity, were ignoring him.

The ships' carpenters went to work putting together a shallop, or schooner, a boat capable of sailing inland waters that had been built in sections back in England and carried across the Atlantic in the hold of the *Susan Constant*. While this was taking place the restless, curious Smith, eager to face the challenge of the forest, went ashore. He took with him a party of thirty men, and Ned and Thaddeus were so anxious to see the wilderness that he included them in the group, even though it was obvious from the attack of the previous night that the wilderness might well prove unfriendly.

Smith's zest for discovery was greater than his caution, and he pushed inland, marching his little band beneath trees so tall that he later wrote of them as a "cathedral." Finding a narrow but distinct trail that, apparently, had been made by human beings, he followed it, and the party came at last to a clearing where a large number of Indian warriors were roasting oysters. The savages fled into the wilderness at the approach of the strangers. The Englishmen promptly ate the oysters, which were larger and more delicate in flavor than any they had known at home.

The shallop was launched on the morning of April 28, and,

with Newport in command, a party went out to explore the south shore of Chesapeake Bay. Several landings were made, and the men were delighted to find oysters and mussels in abundance. They also made their first acquaintance with the clams of North America and found them delicious. There were spring flowers everywhere, and everyone agreed that the huge, wild strawberries were at least three or four times as large as those grown in England.

"We have found the true Garden of Eden," the starry-eyed Wingfield told his fellow gentlemen-adventurers.

"Man must create his own Eden," John Smith replied, and his sensible answer did not make him more popular with his colleagues.

The ships were anchored at the mouth of the stream that Smith named the James River, and the countryside seemed perfect for the establishment of a permanent site. The sands of the beaches were white, the forests of pine and spruce and fir were fragrant, and Nature yielded food in abundance. There were fish in the sea and shellfish in the shallows, the forest was alive with wildfowl and game, and berries, wild onions and other edible plants were at hand for the taking.

Only the threat of hostility from the savages marred the prospect of perfection, and both Newport and Smith were determined to establish friendly relations with the Indians. Wingfield spoke sternly of driving the natives from the area, and his belligerent attitude was strongly supported by Ratcliffe, Archer and Kendal. But Smith and Newport knew that a company of one hundred and fifty could not, in the long run, win a campaign against warriors who might number in the thousands.

So, ignoring Wingfield and his friends, they planned to handle matters in their own way. On April 30 they unexpectedly had their chance. A party of colonists led by Newport and Smith came face to face with a large group of Indians at the crest of a sand dune. Englishmen and savages alike were too startled to move for a moment, and then the braves turned to flee.

But Newport and Smith called out to them, indicating in broad pantomime that they intended the natives no harm. The Indians, who were wearing only loincloths, were impressed by the obvious sincerity of these ferocious, bearded men in steel corselets and helmets. The savages paused, and at last Newport and Smith were able to coax them to return. Prepared for just such a situation, the two Englishmen quickly distributed beads, bracelets and mirrors, and gradually the warriors relaxed.

Smith and Newport suggested they eat together, and not only was the invitation accepted, but the Indians provided venison and bear bacon for the occasion. That night marked the beginning of a new era. Savage North American natives who had never before seen pale-skinned foreigners and Englishmen visiting alien shores three thousand miles from home sat down together to a feast of roasted meat and shellfish.

Ned and Thaddeus sang several songs popular in London, and were accompanied on a flute by one of the company's bricklayers, who had an ear for music. The Indians returned the compliment by dancing, and then produced clay pipes, which everyone smoked. Newport sent to the *Susan Constant* for knives and axes, which he handed out as parting gifts, and when the Indians finally went off into the forest, they left as friends. For the immediate future, at least, the threat of Indian attacks had been greatly diminished. Fears and suspicions on both sides had been stifled, if not vanquished, and there was at least the hope that it might be possible to work out mutually satisfactory arrangements that would enable the colonists to live in peace with their new neighbors.

During the next week a thorough exploration was made of the countryside in the immediate vicinity, and the Indians not only brought the settlers food for barter, but offered their services as guides, too. Smith and Newport, who shared the mistaken beliefs of Archdeacon Hakluyt, Henry Hudson, and many others, that the rivers of Virginia emptied into the Pacific Ocean a short distance to the west, were disappointed to learn that the natives knew of no such rivers. But so firm was this concept in the minds of early seventeenth-century men of learning that neither Smith nor Newport was able to abandon the thought, and they remained convinced that the savages were mistaken.

May 7 was another significant day. A small party led by Percy saw corn growing in the fields outside a small Indian village, and with the consent of the natives took several ears back to the main company. By this time everyone had eaten cakes made by the savages, but until now no one had quite known the principal ingredient. The importance of the discovery was vital to the future of Englishmen in the New World.

American corn, or maize, was totally unknown in Europe, and grew nowhere but in the Americas. "Corn," as the word was loosely used in England and elsewhere, was an informal name for wheat. Many of the settlers immediately became aware of the magnitude of Percy's find. Here, seemingly grown with little effort, was a nourishing grain which flourished in the soil of Virginia.

While the fussy Wingfield experimented with ways to make corn palatable to his delicate tastes, John Smith, acting as usual on his own initiative, not only put in a supply of corn by trading with the savages, but made it his business to learn how the natives of the area planted the unfamiliar grain. His foresight, combined with his insistence that the colonists plant corn themselves at the first opportunity, saved Jamestown from starvation in the next year.

In mid-May a violent quarrel erupted in the Council and almost destroyed the settlement before it was really founded. The time had come to select a site for the building of a town, and Wingfield, utilizing to the full his authority as President, selected ground that was a spongy marsh. John Smith immediately protested, claiming the site would be injurious to health and impossible to defend. The stubborn Wingfield insisted that he had made his choice and that the subject was closed.

But John Smith was a fighter, and although Wingfield ordered him to be silent or face arrest on grounds of insubordination, he refused to be quiet. His arguments were so logical and reasonable that the other members of the Council, including his enemies, finally saw the wisdom of the points he was making and voted with him to reject Wingfield's site and select another on the peninsula that would be centrally located, could be defended by natural water boundaries as well as man-made forts, and commanded a view of the approaches from the sea.

Wingfield gave in with poor grace and went to work drawing up a building plan. Archer, meantime, made his own plan and proudly presented it to the Council, too. Newport, Smith and Gosnold quickly saw that neither scheme was practical. Both Archer and Wingfield proposed grandiose buildings laid out in the manner of large English towns, with broad boulevards, unnecessary public edifices and other extravagances that failed to take into consideration the fact that the community would be located on the fringe of a mighty forest.

It would be impossible to defend either Wingfield's town or Archer's against Indian assaults or attacks from the sea made by Spaniards, Frenchmen or the dreaded pirates of the West Indian Islands, who were fugitives from justice and preyed on honorable men of all nationalities.

While Wingfield and Archer argued and quibbled, tearing each other's ideas to pieces, John Smith considered the best method of presenting a plan for a compact, easily defended community that could be expanded as the colony grew, and would be close to fields of corn, other grains and vegetables. His colleagues showed him no gratitude in return for his fight to select a reasonable site, and instead were even more bitterly opposed to him than they had been earlier. So he realized they would unite to veto any ideas he might present now.

Feeling angry and frustrated because of the need to work indirectly, he made use of his artistic talents to draw a neat ground plan, or primitive blueprint, of the Jamestown he envisaged. He showed it to the two men who were sympathetic toward him, Newport and Gosnold, and both saw that it was infinitely superior to the plans of the others. At Newport's suggestion they waited until Wingfield and Archer exhausted each other and their supporters. Then Gosnold finally intervened and presented Smith's plan as his own.

Not knowing its source, the members of the Council accepted it by unanimous vote, and not until too late did they learn the true identity of the author. Wingfield made one major modification in the plan, and refused to authorize the erection of a fort. Any defense measures undertaken by the colonists, he declared, might alarm the Indians and cause the savages to launch an attack on the colony. Therefore, he said, the only real defense was to prove to the natives that the Englishmen had peaceful intentions.

When Smith argued in favor of putting up a fort, the stubborn streak in Wingfield stiffened. He vetoed the idea of erecting a palisade, or wall of saplings, around the town. And he gave strict orders forbidding parades, military exercises or any gestures the Indians might consider provocative.

Even Gabriel Archer thought the President was going too far in his efforts to avoid trouble, and that, by demonstrating meekness, was actually encouraging the savages to become belligerent.

But Wingfield would not budge and refused to approve any defense preparations other than the bending of tree branches in the shape of a crescent, a notion given him by the military "expert," Kendal.

Smith, Newport and Gosnold were disgusted and made no secret of their joint opinion that Kendal's idea was absurd and useless. But Wingfield insisted the town be surrounded by crescent-shaped branches planted in the ground. His attitude revealed him to be stupid as well as ignorant, and the commoners laughed at him behind his back. His decision to adopt Kendal's "defense plan" robbed him of the respect due the President, and thereafter he found it difficult to command obedience.

Ned and Thaddeus wanted to giggle whenever they saw him, and sometimes were forced to cover their faces with their hands. Older men were less discreet, and often grinned at both Wingfield and Kendal in open contempt. So the very foundation of authority so essential to the success of the enterprise was undermined at the outset.

Active construction work began on May 14, and every ablebodied member of the company took part in the joint effort, chopping down trees, trimming them and uprooting stumps before the stonemasons, carpenters and bricklayers went to work

on the actual construction of the slant-roofed cottages. Only
three buildings were erected for the use of the whole community. One was the church, complete with a spire. Another
was the warehouse for supplies brought from England and
provisions obtained from the natives. And the third was an
arsenal, where the cannon and gunpowder were stored. Smith
and Newport hoped that, in time, they could wear down Wingfield's opposition and convert the arsenal into a fort.

The cottages put up for the commoners were compact but
surprisingly cheerful, each containing a chamber in which four
to six men would sleep, and a small living room. The houses of
the gentlemen-adventurers were slightly larger, with sleeping
accommodations for one or two. It was agreed that all cooking
for the entire community would be done in stone-lined pits in
the "common," onto which all of the houses faced.

Percy and Martin joined with Gosnold and Newport in sup-
porting Smith's demand that ground also be prepared for the
immediate planting of cereals and vegetables. Wingfield and
the other gentlemen-adventurers scoffed, claiming that the
abundance of food made it unnecessary for the colony to en-
gage in any agricultural efforts. Smith's reply was devastatingly
effective. The savages, who had been in the area for a long time,
perhaps for centuries, had found they had to work in order to
eat, he said. So Englishmen could learn a lesson from primitive
barbarians and act accordingly.

Wingfield reluctantly gave the order to prepare some fields
for planting. His attitude almost inevitably made the colonists
less than enthusiastic, and the work on the fields was slow. But
the President refused to punish the slovenly, and as a consequence no crops were planted before the hot summer arrived.

Newport was keeping in mind the directions of the expedition's financial sponsors in London, and set out in the schooner for a journey up the James River in search of the gold, silver and precious gems that the noblemen wanted. There were twenty-three in the party, including Smith, who began work on the first of the maps that were destined to win him immortality.

The Virginia weather in early June was perfect, the towering trees on both banks of the broad James provided cool shade, and the fifty-mile sail was idyllic. Word had gone out from the coastal Indians to the members of small tribes in the interior that the firestick-carrying foreigners meant no harm, and savages appeared daily to barter food for the knives, mirrors and beads that Newport was carrying.

The claim of Wingfield and his friends that there was plenty to eat in the area seemed to be justified. Indian warriors brought huge baskets of oysters, clams and lobsters to the schooner. Others came with heaping gourds of strawberries, blueberries —which grew only in America and therefore were unknown to Europeans—mulberries and blackberries. There were nuts, too, which resembled acorns in appearance and were surprisingly crisp and sweet. Braves came to the boat with beans, ready for eating or planting, bread and cake made of cornflour, and one group arrived with wheat cakes, which surprised and pleased Newport and Smith, who hadn't known that the savages raised wheat.

Some warriors appeared with sides of venison, wildfowl that had been snared and, near the coast, the swordfish that the colonists had learned to enjoy in the tropics. The party ate well on its journey, Smith made a clear, accurate map of the river's course for fifty miles, and everyone was awed anew by the majesty of the benign forest.

The expedition suffered only one disappointment: there was no sign of gold, silver or gems anywhere. Smith, who had already started to teach himself the language of the natives, tried to communicate with them on the subject, but the savages looked blank at the mention of the minerals the Englishmen sought. George Percy thought the natives were lying, deliberately, in an attempt to keep the riches for themselves.

The reply, which Percy committed to paper in his account of the colony's early days, demonstrates John Smith's deep and basic understanding of human nature. "The wilderness," he said, "gives these simple people enough for all their wants. They have food to eat, skins and woven reeds to wear, shelter over their heads to shield them from the rain and wind. What need have they for gold and diamonds? Perhaps they would wear ornaments of glittering objects if there were such things nearby, just as our great lords and ladies wear them. But I can't believe the Indians would lie to us. They already have so many of life's good things that gold and diamonds would be of no real value to them."

On May 27 the schooner returned to Jamestown, and the members of the expedition learned that, during their absence, the peace the colony had been enjoying had been shattered. Two nights earlier, while the workers building the houses had been asleep, a huge band of Indians, perhaps as many as four or five hundred, had suddenly descended on them.

A near-miracle had saved Jamestown from annihilation. Ned and Thaddeus had gone down to the beach to search for crabs, hoping to roast some over an open fire before retiring. The two boys had been intent on their search, but stealthy movements of canoes across the James had alerted them, and they had dashed back to the uncompleted town to give the alarm.

Thanks to Wingfield's refusal to build a fort or allow the settlers to carry firearms, the company was unable to defend itself. A dozen Englishmen were wounded by arrows, and two later died of their injuries. Only the quick thinking and swift action of Bartholomew Gosnold saved the colony. He rallied the crew of the *God Speed,* rowed with his sailors to his ship and fired the two small cannon that stood on the main deck. The roar of the guns, the spurts of flame and the belching of smoke terrified the savages, who vanished into the wilderness night as silently as they had materialized.

Wingfield's policy was completely discarded, and work was begun immediately on the defense measures essential to Jamestown's safety. All other building activities were stopped, and everyone concentrated on putting up a stone and wood fort near the point of the peninsula. A strong wall or palisade surrounding the settlement on the other three sides was quickly erected. Firearms were carried at all times, sentry schedules were established so that watches were kept day and night, and those unfamiliar with the use of muskets and pistols were taught marksmanship.

It became evident that only Smith was qualified to act as an instructor. Even though Archer and Kendal used military titles, they soon proved themselves incompetent, and the whole burden fell on Smith. He was able to train Percy and Martin as assistants, however, and they were able to help him give the settlers the rudiments of military training. Men and boys alike took part in the daily exercises, and only the Reverend Hunt was excused. Even the wounded were required to accept instruction as soon as their health permitted, and with the memory of attack still fresh in the minds of everyone, the settlers labored in earnest to prepare for any new emergency.

Wingfield was incapable of coping with the situation, and the whole Council devoted a great deal of thought to the question of who had been responsible for the attack. The war party had been made up of a far larger number of braves than the few small tribes living in scattered coastal villages could muster; it appeared that the assault had been made by a more powerful, secret foe.

Some of the friendly Indians of the immediate neighborhood were questioned but were reluctant to talk. It became clear that they knew something but were afraid to speak. When the military training program was sufficiently advanced for Martin and Percy to take at least temporary command of the militia, Smith devoted all his energies to solving the problem. He visited several of the nearby villages, freely handed out gifts and simultaneously threatened the savages with his pistols. At last he pieced together the information so vital to the colony's security.

Although the Englishmen hadn't known it, they had established their colony a distance of one to two days' march through the forest from the headquarters of a powerful sachem, or chief, whose nation dominated most of Virginia and had become the overlords of the weaker tribes. These people, the Chickahominy, were taller and more ferocious than the other Indians of the area, and resented the presence of intruders. Their sachem, Powhatan, apparently ruled with a heavy hand, for the coastal Indians demonstrated deep-seated dread whenever they mentioned his name.

Smith reported his findings to the Council, and everyone, including the muddleheaded Wingfield, agreed that an immediate attempt should be made to win the friendship of Powhatan and his Chickahominy. Smith was the only one of the gentlemen-adventurers who volunteered to lead an expedition to the

Indian town, and for once the others were only too happy to yield leadership to him.

Many of the commoners expressed a willingness to follow Captain Smith anywhere, but he decided it would be unwise to march a large body of armed men through the wilderness. The Chickahominy might think he was leading a military expedition against them, and if they tried to repel the intruders, it would be impossible to conduct peace negotiations.

He therefore chose only five men to accompany him. They took enough food with them for the entire journey into the interior and back, as Smith wanted no discharge of firearms to alarm the Chickahominy. The party also carried several sacks filled with gifts.

The courage of Smith in undertaking such a mission caused the beginnings of a change in heart toward him on the part of the other leaders. It was difficult not to admire him, and Ratcliffe, among others, was heard to praise him for the first time. Only Wingfield, jealous of his authority as President and annoyed because someone else was in the limelight, remained remote.

The group of six started off toward the interior immediately after an early breakfast on a bright, warm morning and headed into the forest. Smith was uncertain of the exact location of the Chickahominy town, but had been told the general direction by the coastal Indians and hoped to find signs of habitation that would lead him to Powhatan.

This journey was Smith's first really long march on foot through the wilderness, and he was alert to every subtle nuance. The Englishmen had commented frequently on the silence of the forest, but Smith noted that, if one listened sharply, the woods were alive with sound. Underbrush crackled, indicating the presence of animals in the vicinity; occasionally there was a faint whirring of wings as surprised birds took sanctuary in flight. Sometimes, too, a dead branch fell to earth with a faint thud, and the rippling of water over rocks in a swiftly flowing brook sounded like pleasant, soft music.

What made civilized men uncomfortable in the New World forest, Smith decided, was the absence of other human beings. He was not as yet sufficiently familiar with the wilderness to observe the tiny signs that other men had been in the vicinity. And sometimes he had the feeling he was being watched, yet he could hear or see no one. Still another unique quality of the forest contributed to the lack of ease he and his companions felt. They were hemmed in by trees on all sides, and there were no open spaces of consequence, no real break in the solid, ever present world of pine and oak and elm. It was small wonder he sometimes had the feeling he was in prison and couldn't escape.

After a long day's march, broken only by short rests, Smith and his men halted for the night beside the shore of a small, cool lake. There they caught several fish, and as they had no desire to conceal their presence in the forest from the Chicka-hominy, they built a fire and roasted the fish on it. They also consumed large quantities of the pickled beef and bread they had brought with them from Jamestown.

That night they slept on beds of fragant pine needles, Smith keeping his unsheathed sword and loaded pistols close at hand, the men holding their muskets within easy reach. But their slumber was not disturbed, and in the morning, after a break-fast of more fish, pickled beef and bread, washed down with clear lake water, they started out again.

After an hour or two of a rapid march they slowed their

pace to search for signs of human habitation. But the forest remained dark and yielded no clues. Smith, who had been confident he would be able to locate the Chickahominy town, felt somewhat less certain of success. It would be embarrassing, he thought, if he should be forced to return to Jamestown without finding the headquarters of the powerful Indian nation.

Twice he shed his armor to climb a tall tree and survey the area, but there was no gap in the forest, which spread out in all directions, no telltale smoke from cooking fires. He decided to proceed still farther before admitting defeat.

Suddenly, a short time before noon, a party of a dozen warriors armed with knives and sharp-pointed spears materialized out of the wilderness, so close at hand that it was impossible for the Englishmen to organize an effective defense. Before they could raise their muskets to their shoulders the savages were upon them, scattering them with well-aimed spear thrusts.

Smith whipped out his sword and drew one of his pistols, but the majority of the braves had closed in on him, and his gestures were futile. One husky warrior caught him around the neck from behind, two others pinned his arms to his sides, and his weapons fell to the ground, unused and useless.

The Indians were taking care not to harm him, and it quickly became obvious they were concentrating on him alone. They bound his hands and feet, then strung him on a pole, hanging by his wrists and ankles.

Meanwhile the colonists, seeing what was happening to their leader, were too terrified to come to his aid. The warriors apparently had no interest in capturing them, and to their everlasting shame, they made no attempt to rescue him. Cowering in the underbrush, they watched in horror as the half-naked warriors disappeared into the forest with their trussed captive.

VI

CAPTAIN JOHN SMITH'S agony was excruciating. His arms felt as though they were being torn from their sockets, a deep pain penetrated to the marrow of his thigh bones, and he thought his wrists and ankles were on fire. But his captors ignored his suffering, and still carrying him trussed, they marched for hours through the forest.

Finally, about an hour after sundown, they passed fields of corn and wheat, patches of beanstalks and vines heavy with yellow squash. Smith was only partly conscious, but roused himself when they carried him into a large clearing. Impassive old squaws and elders sitting before clay huts and tents of animal skins watched as he was taken past them. Dogs barked and circled the bearers, sometimes nipping at the helpless Englishman, and small children, some armed with sticks, darted in and out, brushing Smith and the warriors.

A score of young braves emerged from a longhouse of rough logs and formed a protective escort around the prisoner. Smith, trying to focus, caught glimpses of many such longhouses, and when he saw clusters of young women standing outside some of them, realized that several were the dwellings of maidens.

He was dumped to the ground, the bonds at his ankles were cut, and, his hands still tied behind his back, he was driven past a complex of buildings set apart from the rest. Even though his pain was still intense and the braves were prodding him with their spears to force him to move more rapidly, he made a supreme effort to see and observe everything of importance. His guess, based on his visits to smaller Indians villages, was that he was passing the huts of Powhatan and his family.

Suddenly, in the entrance to one of these large huts, he became aware of a sympathetic face. Blinking hard, he looked again and saw a little girl of about ten years, wearing a calf-length dress of woven reeds that had been dyed red, green and blue. Her long black hair streamed down her back to her waist, and her fists were clenched. In her dark eyes he saw pity and, even more, a sense of indignation that any fellow human should be treated so harshly.

As rapidly as she had appeared, she vanished from sight.

The warriors forced Smith onto a dusty field, its earth made barren by the tramping of countless feet. At the edges stood a few stunted pines, and at one end was a mound of boulders that rose about ten or twelve feet into the air. While Smith stood, swaying, the braves cut the thongs at his wrists, and all at once he realized that hundreds of savages had followed the little procession to the field. Old men and women, warriors and squaws in their prime, as well as the younger braves and maidens, were lining the field on all sides.

The Englishman's captors hauled off his helmet, steel breastplate and chain-mail shirt. Then, forcing him to the ground, they removed his boots. When he stood again the Indians were silently facing the boulders, and he looked, too. Seated near the crest of this primitive throne was a middle-aged warrior with hard, chiseled features. He wore a full-length, multicolored cape of feathers, and an ornamental headdress of feathers matched it.

Smith realized that, in all probability, the man was Pow-

hatan, sachem of the Chickahominy and head of a vast confederation of Indian nations. Somewhat lower on the rocks
were two younger men who resembled him, and Smith guessed
they were his sons. At the base of the rocks was a primitive
honor guard of braves armed with knives of copper and axes
with stone heads.

The sachem said something in a harsh, guttural voice, and
when everyone turned, Smith became uneasy and fearful. He
knew he was the reason for the gathering of the Chickahominy,
and he had no idea what might be in store for him.

He straightened, proudly, and awaited his fate.

Thirty or forty warriors trotted onto the field as a drum began to beat; they formed into two lines about four or five feet
apart. All were carrying thick, short sticks, and the braves who
had captured Smith dragged him to one end of the line. The
warriors in the double row were staring at him with expressions
that caused a chill to creep up his back. At the far end of the
line was the pile of boulders, where Powhatan had stationed
himself, and the prisoner would be made to run a gantlet between the two rows.

The braves prodded him forward with their spears, and
Smith knew he had no choice. Steadying himself, he took a
deep breath and began to run.

Blows rained on his head, shoulders and back as he raced,
twisting and dodging, down the narrow lane between the rows
of warriors. He could hear, remotely, the shouts and catcalls of
the men and women, the shrieks of the girls and children, but
he shut them from his consciousness. His one, urgent aim was
to reach the far end of the line alive.

Warriors jabbed at him with their sticks, others tried to trip
him, and the blows that landed on him from both sides were

merciless and jarring. Three times he stumbled, but did not lose his momentum and managed to keep moving forward. The ordeal seemed endless, and he gasped, sucking air into his lungs as he tried to escape from the cruel ordeal.

At last, miraculously, he reached the end of the line and pitched headlong onto the ground. He was dazed, scarcely able to think coherently, and so exhausted he could not move. But it was enough, for the immediate present, not to be subjected to more blows.

Then rough hands grasped him and hauled him up onto the rocks. He struggled feebly but lacked the strength to put up more than a token resistance as several warriors stretched him out on the incline. Powhatan said something curtly in his grating voice, and Smith looked up to see the sachem's sons standing above him, heavy clubs in their hands. When they raised the weapons into the air above his head he knew they were going to kill him, and there was literally nothing he could do to save himself.

Before the two warriors could smash his head, however, the small, agile girl Smith had seen earlier broke through the honor guard cordon and threw herself across the prisoner's body, the child protecting his head with her own.

The drum stopped beating, the crowd fell silent, and Powhatan said something in a stern voice.

The child replied at length, and the stunned Smith realized, even though he could make out only an occasional word, that she was pleading for him.

The sachem's sons stood patiently, waiting for the order to remove the girl and carry out the execution.

Then Powhatan smiled and spoke in a surprisingly gentle voice.

John Smith was aware, as he lost consciousness, that his life had been spared.

For many weeks John Smith remained at the town of the Chickahominy, recuperating from his trial, his status changed from that of a condemned prisoner to one of an honored guest. He slept in a hut of his own on a bed of pine boughs, an old squaw brought him food morning and evening, and when he recovered his strength sufficiently, he was allowed to wander where he pleased in the town. He spent much of his time learning the language of the savages, and spoke at length each day with Powhatan's eldest son, Opachisco, one of the warriors who had stood above him with a club in hand.

But his most frequent visitor was the child who had saved his life. He learned that she was Powhatan's only daughter, his favorite child whom he could refuse no favor, and that her name was Pocahontas. As nearly as he could glean, she was nine years old. She made painstaking efforts to teach him the tongue of the savages, and was an able instructor. He, in turn, taught her English, and they formed a fast friendship. From the child Smith learned much that would prove useful to him in his future dealings with the Indians. He absorbed a great deal of information about their customs, but far more important than all else, he began to understand their thinking.

In return he told Pocahontas about his own land across the great sea, and about the God of the English. She was fascinated, and he promised to give her a Bible at the first opportunity, a promise he kept.

Not until he was strong enough to travel back to Jamestown did he see Powhatan again, but at last the sachem summoned him to a private audience. The meeting was held in a building

Smith had not visited previously, a large hut that appeared to be the sachem's private dwelling. Except for its size, it was the same, essentially, as the other houses Smith had seen in the town. The inner walls of clay were bare; animal skins covered the window openings and entrance, and could be pulled back to admit light and air. The "floor" was hard-packed earth, and five or six pine-bough beds lined the walls. On one wall were several strips of white birch bark on which words had been printed in English with a burned stick or a bit of charcoal, so the Englishman knew this was where Pocahontas slept.

Powhatan sat cross-legged in the middle of the hut, and his guest did the same. The sachem smoked a long clay pipe, occasionally passing it to Smith for a puff, a gesture of hospitality that was a virtual guarantee no harm would come to the visitor. Smith, with his flair for foreign tongues, had made sufficient progress in picking up the essentials of the Chickahominy language so that they were able to communicate without difficulty. They talked for almost three hours, and by the end of that time had worked out an agreement that was to prove Jamestown's salvation.

Smith made the sachem a gift of the steel knife he carried in his boot-top, and also presented Powhatan with his sword, one of three he had brought with him to the New World. The flattered and impressed chief of the Chickahominy was, consequently, in a mood to be generous. He knew of the blankets, mirrors and beads the English settlers had used in their barter agreements with the lesser tribes of the coastal area, and was anxious to obtain a supply for his own people, so it was relatively easy for Smith to strike a bargain with him.

Powhatan agreed to trade dried corn, beans, venison and smoked fish for the products of civilization he prized; he would

make four deliveries of the food each year. Smith had no real
authority to conclude an agreement without the specific approval of the Jamestown Council, but he nevertheless settled
the terms. He had learned that if the Indians thought him too
weak to speak for his fellow countrymen, they would refuse to
have anything to do with him. His original capture had been a
direct result of the Chickahominy belief that he was the
"sachem" of Jamestown, and he said nothing to dispel that
illusion.

When the trade terms had been settled, Opachisco was called
in by his father, and squaws brought the three men a meal intended to seal the bargain. The main dish consisted of a highly
seasoned stew, served in a thick clay bowl. There were chunks
of meat in it that Powhatan and his son fished out with their
fingers, so Smith did the same. Then they dipped cornbread
into the savory, herb-flavored gravy and ate it, dripping. By the
time the meal was finished, all three were greasy, so the squaws
brought them gourds of both heated and cold water to wash
their hands and faces. Contrary to the belief of the Jamestown
colonists, Smith was finding that the Indians were exceptionally clean and neat.

Soon thereafter Pocahontas appeared, shyly, and her father
took obvious pride in her growing ability to speak the language
of the foreigners. Smith, genuinely fond of the little girl who
had saved his life at the risk of her own, invited Powhatan to
bring her to Jamestown, along with other members of his
family. The sachem, who was fascinated by the firearms of the
foreigners, wanted to see cannon and muskets at close range,
and quickly agreed.

Late that afternoon the food supplies that were to inaugurate
the trade agreement were packed in wicker baskets, and at

dawn the following morning Smith left for the coast, accompanied by a strong escort of natives. He was acutely aware of the fact that near-disaster had been transformed into a great personal triumph. Thanks to the valor of an exceptionally sensitive little girl, he was still alive, and thanks to his own talents, he had concluded a bargain that would keep Jamestown from starvation for many months.

Captain John Smith's return to Jamestown created the greatest sensation in the colony's short history. The settlers, who had accepted the story of his capture as it had been told to them by the men who had deserted him, believed him dead. Instead, he looked heartier and healthier than ever, and behind him marched thirty-seven husky Chickahominy braves, each carrying large quantities of provisions. It was small wonder that most of the colonists cheered until they were hoarse.

Wingfield, Archer and Kendal, wildly jealous of the success that had made Smith even more popular than he had been previously, stupidly and shortsightedly tried to prevent ratification of the informal treaty. Ratcliffe even suggested that the settlers drive the warriors empty-handed out of the town. John Smith finally lost his temper with his colleagues.

If they denied the validity of his word to Powhatan, he declared, or if they mistreated the braves, the Chickahominy would be certain to declare war on the Englishmen. And although the colonists might win one battle, perhaps two or three, by using their cannon to frighten away the savages, in the long run the Indians would be certain to triumph. Powhatan could command the services of several thousand warriors, and no colonist would be safe once he stepped outside the palisades. It would be impossible to grow crops, put out to sea on fishing trips or make any other attempt to obtain food. The company would be forced to withstand a siege behind the newly erected barricades.

Furthermore, the angry Smith said, if the Council refused to approve the treaty, he would put himself at the disposal of Powhatan and would seek the scalps of the men who had made a mockery of his promises.

His vehemence startled his foes. And men of common sense rallied to his side. Newport and Gosnold heartily agreed with him that the bargain should be kept. Percy and Martin joined them, and the Reverend Hunt, who rarely interfered in political quarrels, said that the treaty was a proof of God's blessing and that it would be a sin if the Council rejected it.

Wingfield and his supporters were voted down. Smith gave the Chickahominy bearers the blankets, cooking utensils, mirrors and trinkets he had promised Powhatan. And, as a special, personal gift, he sent Pocahontas a length of cloth for a dress, a hairbrush and three books, including the Bible.

The future of Jamestown now seemed relatively secure for a time, even though, during Smith's absence, virtually no progress had been made on the planting of crops. Lacking the authority to demand that everyone work on the project he considered so essential to the colony's welfare, Smith decided to set an example. Gentlemen-adventurers believed themselves too aristocratic to labor with their hands, but John Smith suffered from no such delusions.

On a hot midsummer morning he stripped to the waist and, accompanied by Ned and Thaddeus, went out into the fields. There he and the boys worked until sundown, clearing underbrush, weeding and planting. They went out again early the next morning, and by the third day the subtle campaign began to take effect. Men were ashamed that they were doing less than the one leader of the colony whom they respected, less than two boys whose combined strength could not equal that of one adult.

A dozen volunteers appeared and helped with the preparation of the fields and the planting. On the fourth day, fifty men came out from behind the palisades, and by the end of a week Wingfield was complaining that everyone in Jamestown was so busy at farm work that no one was available for the performance of other chores. Smith's one show of temper had taught the President caution, however, and Wingfield took care to say nothing derogatory about the planting in the hearing of the man responsible for it.

Not all of the colonists enjoyed working in the fields. Some members of the company shared the belief of the financial sponsors in London that there were gold and gems ready for the taking everywhere in the New World. These settlers were disillusioned, and they loathed the choice of eating either native foods or the provisions preserved in salt or brine that had been carried on the expedition. The forest frightened them; they were unable to accept wilderness living and longed for the civilization they had left behind.

There were about twenty men in this group, and the Council discussed their problem at several meetings. Archer foolishly advised that they be given special, easy tasks to perform, but Smith argued that it was wrong to coddle them. Every able-bodied man, he declared, was obligated to work hard, and if favors were shown a few because they whined, the spirits of the others would decline and conditions would become chaotic.

Once again his realistic, sensible approach was adopted by the majority, and no special consideration was given the shirkers. They, however, continued to balk. Some pretended to go through the motions of work, while three or four feigned illness. Smith urged that they be punished by cutting down on their food rations, saying they would change their attitude rapidly once they became hungry. The other members of the Council were not inclined to accept such drastic measures, however, and the basic problem remained unsolved.

Smith and the Reverend Hunt were afraid the germs of discontent would spread to the whole community, and privately discussed the matter with Captain Newport, who was beginning his preparations for a return voyage to England.

"There is no place here for the lazy," Smith said emphatically. "We've learned enough about these forests by now to know that only those who are willing and able to tolerate the hardships of the wilderness in good spirits can survive. The whiners and complainers can destroy us all."

"True," Newport replied. "But if the Council won't take disciplinary action against them, what can be done?"

"I suggest they be given a choice," Smith said. "Any man who is unwilling to work should be sent back to England."

Newport agreed, and announced that any colonist dissatisfied with the New World could sail back to London with him. Eleven of the settlers promptly accepted the offer, and Wingfield was furious, claiming their return would be harmful to the reputation of Jamestown in the eyes of the sponsors.

"You're wrong," Smith told him. "What's far more significant is that more than one hundred civilized men and boys have found it possible to come to terms with the forest, and are staying!"

Another problem, vital to the long-range survival of the colony, was far more difficult to solve. The great lords who had invested in the colony were expecting to gain a handsome profit when the *Susan Constant* reached England, but she would be carrying neither precious metals nor gems. Newport hoped to return to Virginia as soon as he could with a variety of badly needed provisions, but supplies were expensive, so it was unlikely that the sponsors would spend fresh sums unless they obtained some immediate return.

Newport asked the Council for a quantity of the New World's most abundant resource, lumber, and Percy, who knew and loved trees, supervised the cutting of prime oak and cedar. Meanwhile Smith went off for the better part of a week to negotiate special barter deals for furs with the Indians, and was particularly successful in his negotiations with Powhatan. He returned with enough bales of beaver and fox pelts to insure a small profit for the sponsors. Although some of the nobles might be disappointed, it was unlikely that they would abandon the venture, and Newport promised to return by the end of the year if he could.

Eight of the colonists had died, and approximately fifteen others who were ill decided they had no heart for continuing the hard struggle for existence in the wilderness. With the eleven shirkers who were to sail on the *Susan Constant,* too, the permanent community would be reduced to one hundred and five men and boys. Gosnold and Ratcliffe were staying, keeping the *God Speed* and the *Discovery* at Jamestown, where both vessels would be used for deep-sea fishing trips. One or two of the gentlemen-adventurers may have felt apprehensive over the colony's future, but pride prevented them from admitting failure or cowardice, so they conquered their fears and remained.

Newport decided to leave the better part of his ship's stores behind, since it was impossible for the settlers to obtain beef.

So his departure was delayed for almost two weeks while hunting parties roamed through the forest in search of deer, wild boar and smaller game.

John Smith headed one of these parties and, already a veteran, traveled confidently through the wilderness. He was not surprised to discover that the forest was less generous than it had been in the spring. Deer were becoming scarce, and even rabbits and porcupines were difficult to find. Birds, which had themselves vanished, had eaten most of the berries, and the searing midsummer heat had shriveled the rest. The spawning season for shad had ended, and they had disappeared from the rivers, as had trout and other fish. Fortunately, however, oysters, mussels, clams and other shellfish were still plentiful in Chesapeake Bay, and Captain Gosnold, who went out to sea fishing each day, almost invariably returned with a catch of swordfish and giant tuna.

Smith prepared some sketches of the area for Archdeacon Hakluyt and Prince Henry, and carefully drew maps of the waterways he had seen for his friend, Henry Hudson, who was so anxious to find a sea passage through the North American continent. Based on what Smith had learned from the Indians of the headwaters of the James River, he felt certain it did not empty into the Pacific Ocean, and he informed Hudson accordingly. But he was less certain of Chesapeake Bay. Some of the savages had told him of a great river that flowed into the northwest corner of the Bay. It was called the Susquehanna, he told Hudson, and none of the local Indians knew its source, so he thought there was at least a chance that it connected the Atlantic and the Pacific. When he had the opportunity, he wrote Hudson, he hoped to see and explore the river.

At last all was ready for the *Susan Constant*'s departure. Sails and gear were mended, cargo was securely stored in the hold, and the passengers went on board, a few of the shirkers suffering unexpected pangs of remorse now that they were being expelled. Newport held a final meeting with the Council, urging the members to work together in harmony. Then he, too, went on board.

Everyone gathered near the new Fort to watch the ship sail, and most of the colonists were worried and uneasy when they realized their one real link with England was being at least temporarily severed. Ned and Thaddeus became panicky when the *Susan Constant,* her sails filling, glided smoothly and silently toward the open sea. Both boys instinctively looked toward John Smith for protection, and both felt better.

Captain Smith was relaxed, certain he could cope with the New World's terrors, and actually smiled as he watched the *Susan Constant* disappear from sight.

VII

LESS THAN TWENTY-FOUR HOURS after Captain Newport sailed, Jamestown's troubles began.

President Wingfield created some of the problems himself. Three braves of the small, belligerent Pamunkey tribe eluded the sentries, climbed over the palisades and were trying to break into the storehouse when caught. Wingfield wanted them executed on the spot, but John Smith insisted on questioning them, and learned they had tried to steal from the Englishmen for only one reason. Food was becoming scarce, and they were hungry.

Smith released the warriors on his own authority, knowing the Pamunkey would be certain to attack if three of their braves were executed. He expected Wingfield to make a scene, but the President was too disturbed by the news of food shortages to think or care about anything else.

Not bothering to consult the Council, Wingfield announced that the settlers would have to pull in their belts. Henceforth, he decreed, each colonist would be limited to a half-gourd of wheat or corn flour each day, together with a cup of barley. Smith, supported by virtually all the other Council members, argued in vain that the ruling was foolish, as the storehouse was filled with the supplies he had brought back to the colony from the town of the Chickahominy, and more would be forthcoming in the near future.

Wingfield wouldn't listen. If grain and meat were scarce, he said, the Chickahominy would not be able to keep their bargain. So the supplies in the storehouse would be stretched. The Council outvoted him, but he had the only key to the building in which the provisions were kept, so his was the final word. Everyone grumbled, and the colonists were in a state of near mutiny when it was discovered that supplies of salt were running unexpectedly low. The barley was boiled in water to make it palatable, but was tasteless unless seasoned with salt. John Smith solved that problem by marching a small company to a deer lick he had noted a few miles from Jamestown, and the men returned with enough salt to satisfy the colony's needs for a year.

Suddenly, two weeks later, a strange sickness afflicted the settlers. Whether the semistarvation diet was responsible, as some claimed, or whether the colonists were stricken by an affliction that sometimes decimated the Indian tribes of the area was an unanswered question. Far more important than the cause was the effect of the disease. There was no known cure for it, and it was capricious, sometimes killing the strong but sparing the weak.

Only ten members of the community remained healthy, among them Smith and Kendal. Nine others, including Ned, recovered after a few days of illness. The burden on these nineteen was almost intolerable. They nursed the sick, stood sentry duty and did all of the town's chores. Smith later wrote that they were so weakened by their long hours of arduous work and insufficient food that they scarcely had the strength to bury the dead.

The two healthy members of the Council shared the custodianship of the storehouse key, and one night the crisis was compounded. Smith, who had worked for forty-eight hours without rest, was walking toward his cottage to snatch a few hours of sleep when he saw Kendal disappearing into his own house with large quantities of food he had just stolen. Smith forced him, at pistol point, to return the provisions and threatened him with a public trial if he repeated the crime.

Kendal promptly twisted the facts of the story to suit himself, and told the other members of the Council, who were recuperating from the sickness, that Smith had bullied and mistreated him without cause. Some of the gentlemen-adventurers believed Kendal, but others had revised their opinions of the two principals and supported Smith's account.

Death struck the community blindly and furiously and prevented the feud from becoming worse. On August 22, 1607, the distinguished Captain Bartholomew Gosnold, who five years earlier had been the first Englishman ever to explore and chart large sections of the North American coastline, died in his sleep.

Captain Ratcliffe slipped into a coma and was not expected to live, but recovered consciousness after five days, his fever broken. Then commoners began to die, and a feeling of panic swept through the community. Smith curbed it with the aid of Percy, the Reverend Hunt and Martin, who were convalescing. But the panic became infinitely worse when John Smith was stricken with the disease. He fell ill at a time when the survivors were recovering, and the frantic colonists believed, with good reason, that Jamestown was doomed if he died.

For a time Kendal was in charge of affairs, and when Wingfield recovered, they administered the business of Jamestown together. The chaos became worse. Kendal freely drank the brandywine that was saved for strictly medicinal purposes, and he raided the storehouse regularly. It was difficult to imagine that Wingfield was unaware of his activities, but the complicity of the President was never actually proved.

The dazed survivors recovered and took stock of their frightening situation. In all, forty-six men had died, and John Smith was in a critical condition.

All of the English provisions were gone. The last of the pickled beef, wheat flour and minced mutton had vanished. There was nothing in the storehouse except the venison and smoked fish, parched corn and beans that Smith had obtained from the Chickahominy.

Council members and commoners alike were horrified, bewildered—and then violently angry. Something had to be done, but the one natural leader of the community, Smith, was lying unconscious in his bed.

Thaddeus, who had himself just recovered, confided to Ned that it might have been better if he had died.

Only the firm intervention of the usually gentle Reverend Hunt prevented the outraged colonists from lynching Kendal and Wingfield.

Leadership was desperately needed in this time of emergency, and Captain Ratcliffe, who had amazing recuperative powers and swiftly recovered his health, showed leadership of a sort. The members of the depleted Council met at his instigation, dismissed Kendal and ordered his immediate arrest.

There was no jail in the town at that time, so Kendal was locked in a cabin on Ratcliffe's ship, the *Discovery*, his ankles and wrists manacled. Then guards were posted to make certain he could not escape.

The commoners were not yet satisfied and demanded that Wingfield be made to pay a penalty for his negligence. Martin and Percy, the moderate, somewhat timid members of the Council, were reluctant to depose the President, feeling that the dignity of the office itself would be tarnished. But Gabriel Archer, now restored to health, assumed he would be elected in Wingfield's place, and insisted that the will of the people be obeyed.

The Council met secretly while Wingfield was asleep in his own cottage, dismissed him from office by unanimous vote, removed him from his Council seat and ordered that he, too, be placed in confinement. He was marched to the *Discovery* and locked in a cabin, but because no proof could be found that he had engaged in criminal activities, he was not manacled.

John Smith continued to hover near death. He was the choice of the commoners for President, and the Reverend Hunt, Percy and Martin favored him, too. But no one knew whether he would recover, and active, immediate leadership was required.

The Council members cast secret ballots, in writing. To the infinite disappointment of the embittered Gabriel Archer, Ratcliffe was elected as Acting President.

As his first act, Ratcliffe sent out a fishing party on the late Captain Gosnold's *God Speed*. But the season had changed, storms churned up the Atlantic coast from the West Indian Sea, later to be called the Caribbean, and day after day the fishing party returned empty-handed.

Ratcliffe's principal concern was the strengthening of the town's defenses. He lived in mortal fear of an attack by savages, and he forced the settlers to build a new tower on the Fort and start a second palisade just inside the first.

Everyone, even young boys like Ned and Thaddeus, thought the colonists should be concentrating their attention on gathering food supplies for the coming winter. But Ratcliffe refused to listen to advice from anyone, and became enraged when others tried to reason with him. On more than one occasion various members of the Council and some of the commoners, too, thought they detected the odor of brandywine on his breath, but no one was in a position to question him closely.

John Smith became delirious and, while out of his mind, called out to his parents, who had been dead for a number of years.

Thaddeus, having recovered from the sickness, was believed immune to it, and when he begged for the right to nurse Smith, the Council granted him permission. But everyone thought Smith's days were numbered, and even the Reverend Hunt gave up hope. The boy moved into Smith's cottage, however, and remembering how thirsty he had been while ill, fed the Captain sips of water every few minutes.

Gabriel Archer decided to conduct some negotiations of his own with the local Indians and made three trips out of Jamestown, all of them unsuccessful. His manner was arrogant, and he antagonized the tribes of the vicinity. Angry and frustrated, he decided to stake his reputation on a longer journey to the headquarters of the Chickahominy, but his humiliation was compounded when warriors appeared from the forest and refused to let him proceed toward their town. As nearly as he and the men with him could glean, Powhatan considered Smith the sachem of the Englishmen and refused to deal with anyone else. Not even Archer had the courage, at this juncture, to let the word be passed to Powhatan that Smith was critically ill.

Kendal and Wingfield found a way to communicate with one another on board the *Discovery* and began plotting to take over the colony, if possible, or sail back to England on the ship if all else failed.

Acting President Ratcliffe, still obsessed with the colony's defenses, put every able-bodied man to work on the inner palisade. Percy protested that game would soon disappear from the forest as winter approached, but Ratcliffe refused to send out hunting parties.

Then, one afternoon, John Smith's fever broke. He slept for a few hours, opened his eyes and calmly told Thaddeus, who was sitting beside his bed, that he was hungry.

The good news was relayed to the whole community, and the patient was given a nourishing Indian broth of clams and mussels, a dish he had long enjoyed. The other members of the Council visited him and brought him up to date on all that had been happening in Jamestown. Smith made no comment, and they thought he was too weak to think clearly, but when they finished their recital he proved them wrong.

Asking for a quill pen and paper, he wrote a brief note to
Pocahontas, worded in simple English, requesting her to inform
her father that, although he was unable to make the journey to
the town of the Chickahominy himself, he was sending friends
with a variety of goods for purposes of barter. Then he told
Acting President Ratcliffe to put Percy in charge of an expedition to the town, and stressed that Ned and Thaddeus should be
members of the group. The presence of the boys in the party,
he explained, would signify to the ever suspicious savages that
the colonists' intentions were peaceful. Finally, he directed that
Percy take a number of large kettles to the Indians, as well as
iron ladles and other cooking utensils he knew the natives
would admire.

Before dropping off to sleep again, Smith had a few private
words with Thaddeus and Ned. The establishment of a permanent English colony in the New World, he told them, depended
on the ability of the settlers to achieve a genuine understanding
with the savages. The one key to that understanding, he
stressed, was communication, and he urged the boys to take advantage of every opportunity to learn the tongues of the Chickahominy and the other tribes. The long-range future, he said,
depended on them, and on Indian children like Pocahontas, who
was studying English.

Percy left for the interior at daybreak the next morning, and
in five days he and his party returned, accompanied by more
than a score of warriors carrying provisions from the Chickahominy stores. Although the settlers' diet might be restricted
and monotonous in the months ahead, no one would starve.

Ned and Thaddeus reported a personal success, too. Pocahontas had agreed, eagerly, to teach them the language of the
Chickahominy in return for English lessons, and in a few weeks

would be coming to Jamestown for the purpose with her brother, Opachisco. They were already able to speak a little Chickahominy, they proudly told Captain Smith, who was delighted with their progress.

Smith himself was recuperating swiftly from his illness and was already sufficiently recovered to make his influence felt. He made a careful inventory of the storehouse contents, and in order to prevent the stealing of food by unprincipled leaders, he suggested the adoption of a new system. Henceforth, he said, two locks should be placed on the storehouse door, one key to be kept by the President and the other by someone else on the Council, preferably a member elected by his colleagues.

Everyone except Ratcliffe approved the idea, but he was afraid his own guilt might be discovered if he protested too strongly, so he accepted the scheme. Smith was elected to serve with him and was given the key to the second lock. Brandywine no longer disappeared, which confirmed the guess of several Council members that Acting President Ratcliffe had been stealing it.

More than ever before Smith now emerged as the real leader of Jamestown. Ratcliffe liked his title, but did not enjoy work, and gave Smith the major share of responsibility for the welfare of the community. Accepting the burden cheerfully, Smith drew up new schedules and initiated a variety of projects.

The best hunters and fishermen were sent out each day to search for food, and as Ratcliffe himself was the most experienced sailor in the colony, he was given the task of putting out to sea each day in the *God Speed.* Men who remained behind in the settlement had enough to keep them busy, too. A close inspection of the houses that had been so hastily erected soon after the colonists had landed the previous spring convinced

Smith they were too flimsy to withstand the rigors of winter. Therefore he ordered them strengthened. When necessary, cottages were razed and new ones built. Particular emphasis was placed on roofs, and he insisted they be made as watertight as possible. A season of heavy rains had started, water was leaking into some of the cottages, and Smith was afraid that many of the colonists, already weakened by the mysterious sickness, might become victims of the ague, which in a later time would be called influenza.

He also canceled work on Ratcliffe's new inner palisade. It would do nothing to bolster Jamestown's defenses, he said, and might even become a handicap in a battle with the savages. Warriors, he explained, might hide themselves in the narrow space between the two palisades, and it would be impossible to dislodge them.

Ratcliffe's feelings were ruffled by the cancellation of his pet project. He was supported by Archer, who was always jealous of Smith, but the other members of the Council had learned to trust Smith's judgment, and the Council ratified his decision. In his private opinion, which he kept to himself at the time, Smith thought that Ratcliffe's projected extension of the Fort would be a waste of effort. Responsibility was making him more tactful than he had been in the past, and rather than openly antagonize Ratcliffe by opposing too many of his ideas, he simply let work on the Fort wait. When he could, he intended to strengthen it in his own way.

Wingfield and Kendal were still being held as prisoners on board the *Discovery,* and Smith believed that the continued detention of two former leaders had a bad effect on the spirits of the entire colony. After thinking about the matter at some length, he decided to visit the prisoners in order to find out if some way might be found to return them to useful employment in Jamestown.

Edward Wingfield greeted Smith with chilly disdain. It quickly developed that he believed Smith his chief persecutor. His attitude was illogical, since Smith had been gravely ill at the time he had been removed from office, and had known nothing of the matter until much later. But Wingfield wouldn't listen to reason, and when Smith, curbing his own temper, offered the former President a chance to rehabilitate himself, Wingfield curtly refused.

He had only one desire, he said. He wanted to return to England at the first opportunity and intended to write a book in which he would "tell the truth about the nefarious Captain Smith."

Imprisonment had made him even more stubborn than he had been previously, and Smith finally realized the talk was accomplishing nothing. It was evident that Wingfield cared nothing about Jamestown's problems and future and was concerned only with himself.

George Kendal displayed a far different attitude. He greeted Smith with surprising amiability, asked him to sit, and apologized for receiving a visitor in such a cramped cabin. Smith was encouraged and removed the shackles from the prisoner's ankles and wrists, believing it would be easier to talk if the man's dignity was restored to him.

The instant the chains fell away, Kendal's manner changed. Suddenly he lunged at his deliverer, his fingers closing around Smith's throat, and they fell together to the deck. Kendal's strong fingers tightened, and he tried to choke his victim to death.

The assault was so unexpected that Smith, unprepared for

physical violence, had no chance to defend himself. Still weakened by his illness, he tried in vain to pry Kendal's fingers from his throat, and he lacked the breath to call out to the guards patrolling the deck.

Never, in many narrow brushes with death, had John Smith felt so helpless—or so enraged. He had come to the *Discovery* hoping to do Kendal a kindness, and was about to lose his life because of the man's vicious trickery. Aware of his weakness and knowing that the little strength he possessed was rapidly ebbing, he realized he had to rely on guile to save himself.

He made a beckoning gesture in the direction of the cabin door, and at the same time twisted his head slightly in an attempt to look at the door. He seemed to be summoning help from someone who, supposedly, had just entered.

His play-acting was good enough to fool Kendal, who glanced toward the door and, briefly, relaxed his hold.

That instant was all the time Smith needed. Rallying his last reserves of strength, he heaved desperately, at the same time bringing his fists down on his attacker's forearms.

Kendal's grip was broken.

Before he could grasp his victim again, Smith rolled over on top of him and, gasping for breath, hoarsely shouted to the guards.

Kendal caught hold of one of the chains, which was lying on the deck, and started to beat at Smith with it as both men struggled to their feet.

Smith abandoned his caution and advanced toward his foe, both fists flailing. He caught Kendal with a hard smash to the cheekbone, doubled him over with a blow to the pit of the stomach and then straightened him again with a punch that landed on the point of his chin.

Kendal dropped the chain to the deck and staggered, glassy-eyed, against the bulkhead just as the two guards burst into the cabin.

John Smith had already subdued the prisoner, who made no protest as the manacles were placed on his ankles and wrists. Kendal was still cursing as the cabin door was locked behind him.

Physically jarred and emotionally saddened by the experience, Smith went ashore. The other Council members were not surprised by Wingfield's attitude, which they had expected. But they insisted that Kendal be punished for his attack.

Smith recommended that he be treated leniently and that the incident be forgotten, saying that he himself had been negligent.

But the others rejected his charitable approach. With the Reverend Hunt abstaining, the Council voted that Kendal be executed by hanging. Smith, who was afraid that personal feuds between the gentlemen-adventurers could lead to similar death sentences in the future, succeeded only in persuading the Council not to take immediate action on its decision. George Kendal continued to live, but on borrowed time.

The colony now devoted its entire attention to the battle for survival. The hunters reported seeing wild turkeys in the forest, but these birds, peculiar to the North American wilderness, were so wily it was impossible for the settlers to shoot them. Smith, who was now able to speak the native tongues fairly fluently, discussed the problem with some of the natives from the coastal villages and learned that the savages set traps for the turkeys. He instructed the colonists to do the same, and they began to net a fair number of the birds.

There was no real improvement in the larder, however. So

many gales roared up from the West Indian Sea in October that
fishing ventures had to be abandoned. The *God Speed* was so
severely damaged in one of these storms that she was rendered
unseaworthy, and Ratcliffe doubted that she could be repaired
by men other than experienced naval carpenters. Smith inspected the battered ship and was forced to agree, although he
proposed that an attempt be made by the colonists themselves
when they found the time.

Late in October Opachisco came to Jamestown as the envoy
of his father, bringing forty warriors with him. Pocahontas was
a member of the party and delighted Smith with the progress
she was making in learning to read the Bible. During the eight
days the Chickahominy party remained in the settlement she
spent most of her time with Ned and Thaddeus, to the mutual
benefit of all three.

By the time the visit ended, Smith later wrote, the boys were
chattering in the language of the savages, Pocahontas spoke a
reasonably intelligible English—and all three youngsters had
become proficient in the fine art of turning cartwheels.

Relations between the adults were more complicated and
delicate. Smith wanted to conceal the precarious state of the
colony's food reserves from the savages, and insisted on showing the Chickahominy generous hospitality, even though forty
newcomers made heavy inroads into the food supplies. If Powhatan knew the Englishmen were depending on the food he
gave them in his trade deals, Smith explained to the other members of the Council, he could starve them whenever he pleased.
It was too dangerous a game to give him that much power over
them.

The colonists staged a military review for their guests on the
final day of the visit. The Council members were apprehensive

because they could put so few men into the field, but they compensated in their demonstration of fire power for their lack of numbers. Percy gave the commands, the militiamen marched up and down in step, and the Chickahominy warriors looked vaguely bored. Then Smith, who was standing beside Opachisco on a hastily erected reviewing stand, signaled to Percy. The militiamen halted, raised their muskets and simultaneously fired high into the air.

Some of the senior braves flinched, and Opachisco was barely able to control himself, but managed to remain impassive.

Acting President Ratcliffe was stationed in the Fort, and when Smith drew his sword in a prearranged sign, the colony's two cannon roared, belching fire and smoke.

The composure of the warriors was shattered. None had ever seen or heard such a frightening man-made spectacle, and braves who had endured countless hardships in battles against their savage foes literally crumpled. Some covered their faces with their hands, several completely lost their composure and threw themselves to the ground, and even Opachisco instinctively held out a hand, as though to ward off a blow.

Gunpowder was precious, but the exhibition, as Percy later wrote, was worth every ounce used. Warriors who had shown contempt for the Englishmen subsided, and Opachisco, who had been cool and polite to his hosts, suddenly began to speak in terms of arranging a peace treaty that would last for all time.

Early the next morning the visitors left for their home, and Smith, as a friendly gesture, accompanied them with an escort of his thirty most accomplished militiamen. The little company consisted of two platoons, one commanded by Percy and the other by Archer. The Englishmen and Chickahominy marched and ate together, and Smith felt he had reason to congratulate himself. Peace with the most powerful Indian confederation in Virginia seemed assured for a reasonable future.

What he failed to take into account was that he had left Jamestown in a vulnerable spot. Perhaps, as Smith believed, there was nothing to fear from other Indians at the moment, since none would have risked incurring the wrath of the Chickahominy. But other, far more insidious enemies were at work, and the tiny settlement was in grave danger of being destroyed.

VIII

THE PLOT WAS the brainchild of George Kendal, who persuaded the weak Edward Wingfield to cooperate with him. Working separately and secretly, they managed to persuade some members of the *Discovery*'s original crew to desert the colony and sail the pinnace back to England. These men, in turn, spoke to some of the sailors from the *God Speed,* who were also weary of trying to cope with the forest. In all, a crew of eighteen was assembled, but neither Kendal nor Wingfield was an experienced ship's master. Both were afraid to ask Ratcliffe to join the conspiracy, however, and decided to sail the ship across the Atlantic themselves.

The departure of Smith, Percy and Archer with the most efficient and loyal of the colonists caused the plotters to speed their plans. This was their great chance, and they knew it. They decided to strike that night, but two of the seamen from the

Discovery balked when they learned they would be under the command of captains who knew little about the sea.

The delay until the following day seemed to be just a minor obstacle, however. Smith and his company were still absent in the forest, and no news of the scheme had been leaked to the other settlers. The plotters decided to catch the afternoon tide, and planned their other moves accordingly.

At noon Kendal and Wingfield were released from their locked cabins, and when Kendal's chains were removed, he took charge of the operation. He went ashore, armed with a pistol and sword, and led his crew in a daring raid on the storehouse. Virtually the entire colony gathered, but no one dared to intervene as the mutineers trained their muskets on the crowd. Sides of smoked venison were carried off to the *Discovery,* as were kegs of beans and parched corn. Showing a brutal lack of concern for the welfare of the men and boys they were leaving behind, the sailors took the better part of the supplies that had been gathered with such painstaking effort.

Acting President Ratcliffe appealed to Kendal and Wingfield to abandon their scheme, and spoke so convincingly that Wingfield seemed on the verge of changing his mind. Kendal, however, silenced Ratcliffe by threatening him with a pistol. The Reverend Hunt made an appeal to the mutineers and begged them in the name of the Almighty to reconsider. Some of the sailors and Wingfield edged toward the onlookers, and it appeared they were taking the clergyman's words to heart.

Kendal knew that unless he acted swiftly, the entire conspiracy might collapse. He was reluctant to fire his pistol at the Reverend Hunt, but had no hesitation in striking him across the face with the butt of the weapon. The clergyman collapsed to the ground, moaning, and no one else had the courage to intervene.

When the supplies had been loaded on the pinnace, Kendal shepherded his crew on board the ship. Wingfield, who looked as though he would burst into tears, was slow to respond, and Kendal prodded him viciously with his pistol.

At this critical moment, as the seamen were running up sail and preparing to cast off, Captain John Smith and his company marched back into Jamestown. Suspecting nothing amiss, Smith, Percy and Archer were stunned, but the colony's military leader reacted instantly to the bold challenge.

Ignoring his own safety, Smith sent the militiamen racing to the Fort, and himself walked slowly toward the pinnace, which had not yet cast off. There was an uneasy stir on the deck of the *Discovery,* and Kendal, furious because he had come so close to success without encountering complications, trained his pistol on his enemy. Smith paid no attention to the threat.

"In the name of King James and the Council of this settlement," he called, "I command you to stop. Disarm yourselves and come ashore at once, or pay the consequences. I'll give you precisely one minute to obey. At the end of that time the cannon in the Fort will sink you, so take your choice."

There was a breathless pause for a moment, then Wingfield and two of the sailors leaped from the deck to the ground, throwing their arms ahead of them.

Suddenly John Smith dropped to the grass, and a split second later the roar of a pistol broke the silence. Kendal's shot sailed harmlessly over his head. Smith leaped to his feet again, and in the same motion drew his own pistol. He aimed and fired it so rapidly that few of the shocked spectators even saw his move.

His aim was remarkably accurate, and Kendal's pistol clattered to the deck.

Smith's swift response ended the mutiny. The sailors came ashore one by one, throwing their weapons ahead of them, as they had been ordered. Meanwhile the militiamen who had hurried off to the Fort raced back, with Percy and Archer leading them.

The last to leave the *Discovery* was the disgruntled Kendal, who was seized by Percy and Archer the moment he stepped ashore. A number of angry settlers started toward him, but Smith waved them back. There had been enough disorder, he said sternly, and demanded that everyone respect the law. The men obeyed him, in spite of their anger at Kendal, and then most of the colonists were sent aboard the pinnace to retrieve the food supplies and return them to the storehouse.

Smith realized he himself had been at fault. Had he not treated Kendal leniently, the mutiny would not have taken place. He had no intention of repeating his error.

A full-scale trial of the mutineers was held that same afternoon. The colonists chose a jury from their own number, and the members of the Council acted as judges, with Acting President Ratcliffe the chief justice. Only the Reverend Hunt was absent; he had gone to bed suffering from a severe cut across his face.

The sailors who had taken part in the escape attempt were given conditional pardons. Ratcliffe warned them, on behalf of the entire Council, that severe punishment awaited any man who strayed again.

The jury debated the fate of Edward Wingfield for a long time, finally deciding he had merely been Kendal's follower. He was sent to a temporary prison in one of the cottages, where he would remain until a strong jail could be built. The jury recommended that he be deported to England on the first ship that called at Jamestown, and the Council issued a formal decree to that effect.

Kendal was tried last, and feeling against him ran so high that judges and jury alike were inclined to dispose of the case quickly. But Smith reminded the court that the law was a prized possession of every Englishman. Kendal, he insisted, was entitled to a full hearing. The record of the case would be examined in London, he said, and those who tried Kendal would themselves be on trial.

His sensible advice was followed, and Kendal was given a remarkably fair hearing. But the verdict was never in doubt. He was found guilty of conspiracy, mutiny and inciting to mutiny, threats against decent, peaceful citizens, an attack against the Reverend Hunt and an attempt to murder Captain Smith.

The jury recommended that he be executed, and the judges unanimously approved. By now it was evening, and the entire community, with the exception of the Reverend Hunt and the sentires standing watch, assembled at the parade ground. A gallows was erected, and George Kendal was hanged, the first Englishman put to death on colonial soil by his fellow citizens.

The accumulation of food supplies was the chief concern of Jamestown during the waning weeks of 1607. As Smith had feared, the crops planted by the colonists were a disappointment, and it became necessary to look elsewhere for provisions. The schooner went off into Chesapeake Bay on several expeditions to obtain shellfish, and the settlers became tired of oysters and clams, but hungry men were in no position to complain. Game completely vanished from the forest, and, in mid-December, the weather became so cold that the ground froze.

Fortunately the cottages were sturdy enough now, and the men gathered stones so that hearths could be built. By early January of 1608 most of the houses were equipped with hearths, and no one succumbed to the ague. In fact, the colonists enjoyed such robust health that the gentlemen-adventurers were puzzled. It was reasonable to assume that men living on the fringe of a raw forest wilderness would be prey to sickness, particularly when they were dressed in rags, had barely enough food to eat and were subjected to the most bitterly cold winter weather that Virginia would know in more than a half-century.

Twelve years later, in 1620, the colonists who settled at Plymouth, in New England, went through a similar experience. Many became ill and died in the first months after landing, but the survivors, who included women and children as well as men, enjoyed exceptionally good health for the rest of their long lives.

The wilderness, it appeared, treated the weak cruelly, but rewarded the strong.

In any event, the men and boys of Jamestown suffered no casualties worse than frostbite during their first long winter in the New World. The execution of George Kendal had sobered the gentlemen-adventurers, and for a time, at least, no new plots disturbed the peace. Acting President Ratcliffe was content to enjoy the glory of his office and leave the real work to others, principally John Smith.

The scrupulously fair trade practices Smith had instituted in dealings with the Indians paid handsome dividends that winter. Smith himself made four or five short journeys into the interior, and always returned with meat and grain obtained in barter

with the savages. Like everyone else he dreamed of beefsteak,
but one night, when he had invited Ned and Thaddeus to eat
supper with him in his snug cottage, he told them with a grin
he had become so accustomed to the taste of smoked venison
and unleavened corn bread that he didn't know whether his
appetite for other dishes had been spoiled.

In the near future, he predicted, he and everyone else at
Jamestown would have the chance to find out. He had heard of
a tribe deep in the interior that kept cows, and he hoped to
obtain some from them. The boys' mouths watered as they
thought of beef, milk and butter.

Smith had other, equally startling plans. He hoped to do-
mesticate wild boars, which would assure the colony of regular
supplies of pork, ham and bacon. And if it was true, as he had
been told by the coastal Indians, that the tribes on the north
shore of Chesapeake Bay kept chickens, the settlers would have
eggs and fowl, too, after he made a journey into that part of
the country. Even though the tiny colony of fewer than sixty
men and boys was completely cut off from the civilized world
and forced to endure hardships almost beyond belief, Smith's
spirit was unquenchable.

"This is the land of the future," he told Ned and Thaddeus.
"Once we've learned to adjust ourselves to the wilderness, we'll
prosper on our own. The soil here is so rich we can grow crops
for England's use as well as our own. There's everything in the
New World for man's needs. Once we've harnessed the forests
and the rivers, the meadows and lakes—and, above all, the soil
that can produce the greatest yield on this earth, America will
do more than produce wealth beyond the imagination of the
nobles who dream of gold and diamonds. We have the opportunity to create a new breed of men. Anyone who learns to

meet Nature on her own terms here becomes free in spirit, loses his fear and can hold his head high for all time!"

The promise of the shining future remained remote through the bitter winter of 1607–8, and the colonists considered themselves fortunate to survive. The weather was so cold that game fled south, fish vanished from the rivers and lakes, and even the usually abundant oysters, clams and mussels of the beaches became scarce. Jamestown subsisted exclusively on the provisions Smith had obtained from the Indians. The settlers had worn their clothes thin, and the bolts of cloth in the storehouse were insufficient for their needs. Animal skins were used to make moccasins, trousers and shirts, but only those who had nothing left but rags received new attire. There weren't enough skins to meet the requirements of the whole community. The colonists were warm enough in their cottages, where fires burned night and day in the hearths, but it was torture to step out of doors. Smith had to use all his powers of persuasion as well as the threat of discipline to force the colonists to stand sentry duty and go off to the beaches on shellfish-hunting details.

Almost inevitably, disgruntled Council members began to conspire again. The lesson of Kendal was forgotten, and the gentlemen-adventurers seemed incapable of taking to heart the example of Edward Wingfield, who was languishing in the new jail. Smith felt very weary and discouraged when Percy and Martin came to him with word that Archer and Ratcliffe were thinking of trying to sail the *Discovery* back to England. They would succeed where Kendal and Wingfield had failed, they thought, because Ratcliffe's position as Acting President made it unlikely that anyone would suspect him of chicanery.

Smith promptly confronted the pair, who denied they were

scheming to desert. The realization that he was alert to their plot made it virtually impossible for them to carry it out, but they became his enemies again, reverting to the attitude they had maintained on the long voyage from England to Virginia. They opposed him in many little ways, almost impossible to detect, thus making it far more difficult for him to administer the affairs of the colony efficiently.

Late in March the snows vanished, the ground melted and welcome breezes of warm air made life tolerable again. Smith was prepared for the coming of spring, and immediately put the whole colony to work planting corn and beans he had saved for the purpose. This further depleted the already scarce supplies in the storehouse, which caused a great deal of grumbling. But he flatly refused to compromise. "We can't live forever with the threat of starvation hanging over our heads," he said. "We must grow enough food for our own needs."

The situation was made still more complicated by the fact that the savages had no more food to barter. They, too, had suffered because of the scarcity of game and fish, and needed their reserves of venison, beans and corn for their own use. Hunting parties went out into the forest from Jamestown every day and met with fair success, bringing back enough game for immediate needs, but the settlers literally lived from day to day. No one knew, when the hunters went out each morning, whether there would be anything to eat the following morning. The strain of this precarious existence told on everyone, and even Smith lost some of his buoyant optimism.

Fish had not yet started to run in the rivers, and he was reluctant to let Ratcliffe put out to sea in either the schooner or the *Discovery*. One day, he feared, the Acting President would vanish with a few companions and try to set sail for

England. Therefore both vessels remained at their berths in the James River.

Late one morning in April, 1608, the sentry on duty in the Fort sighted the sails of a ship approaching the settlement, and everyone hurried down to the point. Smith was ready to order the guns manned if the vessel proved to be a pirate or Spanish warship, but when she drew closer the men and boys started to cheer. She was flying the British ensign, and soon they recognized the familiar silhouette of the *Susan Constant*.

Captain Christopher Newport could not have come back to Jamestown at a more opportune time. Spirits had reached their lowest ebb. The storehouse was empty. Most of the colonists were, as Smith put it, "as naked as the savages." Even the gunpowder and ammunition on which Jamestown depended for its defense was almost gone.

The hold of the *Susan Constant* was filled with supplies, and the deck was piled high with barrels and kegs. There was pickled beef and minced mutton, sacks of wheat flour that would make the white bread everyone had been talking about, kegs of herring and sacks of sugar. There were barrels of ale, which Englishmen normally drank with their meals at home, and such delicacies as prunes, raisins and currants.

Several large boxes were filled with stout leather for shoes and boots, and there were enough bolts of wool and linen for the tailor and his volunteer assistants to make new wardrobes for everyone in the community.

John Smith was delighted to receive other items. Newport brought the colonists supplies of gunpowder and ammunition, large quantities of cooking utensils, mirrors and beads to use in trade with the Indians and, far more precious than anything else, packages of peas and seeds to start vegetable gardens in

earnest. Reinforcements cheered the colonists, too. Eight gentlemen-adventurers and more than sixty commoners had come
to Virginia on board the *Susan Constant,* and were joining the
colony.

It was Smith's private opinion, which he expressed to no one
but Newport, that these immigrants would be more of a burden
than a help until they learned the rules of wilderness living and
submitted themselves to the disciplines of a frontier community.
Nevertheless they were made welcome, and their presence was
a guarantee that the colony could hold its own if attacked by
savages.

Everyone was given a twenty-four-hour holiday after the ship
arrived, and then all the settlers, including the newcomers, were
put to work on a schedule that kept them busy from early in
the morning until late at night. The far-sighted Smith had already cleared new fields, and first priority was given to the planting of vegetables, barley and oats. Colonists were sent out into
the forest to chop and trim trees, and the carpenters, stonemasons and bricklayers began to build cottages for the new arrivals. The Fort was strengthened, and the Reverend Hunt's
church was enlarged.

The tailor and his helper began to turn out new clothes,
which were handed out on a basis of need. Some of the veterans,
however, preferred to make themselves shirts, trousers and moccasins of buckskin, now that game was reappearing in the forest.
Newport was surprised, but their attitude seemed natural to
Smith.

"They're at home here," Smith said, "and they want to wear
clothes that are badges of the wilderness." He himself proudly
wore buckskins most of the time, saving his armor for special
occasions.

James Fort in 1609

The Beginnings of the Jamestown Colony

Great care was taken to insure that none of the precious supplies were stolen. On the day that the decks and hold of the *Susan Constant* were emptied of their contents, the most reliable of the colonists were armed with muskets and lined the route from the ship to the storehouse. Newport was in charge of the unloading, and Smith supervised the storing of the goods, with Percy and Martin moving up and down the line, ready to give the order to fire if anyone made a move toward the provisions.

New locks, much stronger than any used previously, were placed on the door of the bulging storehouse, and three keys were now needed to open the entrance. At Smith's request, Newport took one of the keys and agreed to serve as a custodian as long as he remained in the colony.

As soon as the houses were built, all of the new arrivals, gentlemen-adventurers included, were given military training, with Percy acting as drillmaster. Many of the immigrants complained, and it was difficult to blame them. They had been impressed by the tall tales of the mineral wealth they would find in the New World and had heard, too, that native "slaves" would wait on them in a land of plenty. Instead, after an arduous voyage on a small, cramped ship, they were being forced to work eighteen hours each day. The English food that the *Susan Constant* had brought to Jamestown had been stored away, and they were compelled to eat strange, smoked meats, a coarse native grain and unfamiliar fish. The dark, forbidding forest that loomed behind the town terrified them, they were driven by a stern taskmaster, Smith, and to cap their miseries, the settlers who had already spent a year in the New World laughed at their fears.

The new group of gentlemen-adventurers rebelled first, and soon all of the immigrants were clamoring for relief from the chores they had been assigned. Ratcliffe, always anxious to curry favor, was inclined to sympathize with them, but John Smith devised his own ingenious method of curtailing the insurrection.

Everyone was summoned to the parade ground, and the veterans gave a demonstration of their skill with firearms. Small targets were set up at a distance of fifty to one hundred paces, and man after man confidently stepped to the firing line, took aim and hit the mark. After Thaddeus and Ned showed their prowess with both musket and pistol, there was an uneasy silence, and the newcomers were afraid to speak.

Smith, who had taken no part in the exhibition, stepped forward to address them. "One year ago," he said, "none of these men could handle arms, and the boys had never fired a shot in their lives. What they've done, you can do—if you're willing to work. Any of you who find America too alien and primitive are privileged to leave. We won't try to hold you here when Captain Newport sails back to London, and you're entitled to accompany him, if you wish. Until then, you'll earn your keep.

"I'm not going to ask any of you to stay. But I do urge you to become acquainted with the wilderness. Decide for yourselves whether you'll ever feel free in the forests. Give the New World a chance to work her spell. And eventually, with no one telling you what to do, you'll know whether you want to stay."

His advice was so reasonable and fair that the incipient revolt collapsed.

But there were other, equally grave problems that Newport brought with him from England. The great lords who had invested in the colony had refused to accept the realities of the New World, and were more insistent than ever in their demands for gold and diamonds. The crown was proving short-sighted, too, and King James had requested that Powhatan swear an oath of allegiance to him. The very idea was so absurd that John Smith laughed aloud.

It was necessary, however, to go through the motions of obeying orders. Smith and Newport, accompanied by a large party of colonists, made a journey inland and conducted a fruitless search for precious metals. But the trip was not a complete loss. Smith discovered that one of the newly arrived gentlemen-adventurers was a man of considerable talents. Matthew Scrivener was tall and rawboned and looked woebegone, but he was courageous, had an incisive mind and demonstrated crisp executive abilities. It was good to know there was someone to whom a portion of the administrative burden could be given.

The party visited the main town of the Chickahominy, and Newport, in a solemn ceremony, presented Powhatan with several gifts from his "fellow monarch," James of England. These included a cape of purple velvet and a sword with a gold hilt, both of which impressed the sachem. He was somewhat puzzled by a third gift, a canopied bed, which the settlers had carried in sections and assembled for him. Since he had never slept on anything more luxurious that pine boughs, he had no idea what to do with the bed, but nevertheless accepted it graciously.

Newport and Smith tactfully refrained from asking him to swear allegiance to James as his overlord. The mere idea would have offended Powhatan so severely that he might have been tempted to make war against the settlers. Smith's report to the crown on the subject was a masterpiece of evasion, and he gave King James the impression that Powhatan had become his subject, but carefully avoided telling an untruth in so many words.

Pocahontas had mastered English sufficiently by now to converse fluently with the colonists in their own tongue, and her proud father agreed to permit her to accompany the settlers back to Jamestown. He provided her with a strong escort, and Smith cannily took advantage of the occasion to arrange a new barter agreement. Powhatan, flattered by his gifts, gave the Englishmen more generous terms, and the warriors who marched with Pocahontas carried enough grain and meat to feed the colony for a month.

When the party reached Jamestown after a journey through the forest it was discovered that the storehouse was not large enough to hold all of the supplies at hand, so an addition had to be built. Ratcliffe, who was nettled because he had been given no part in the presentation ceremonies, decided to show everyone that he was more than a figurehead. He protested against the erection of the addition, claiming that "more important" projects would have to be put aside and would suffer.

The Council, which had been enlarged to include several of the newly arrived gentlemen-adventurers, was called into session to consider the question. Only Gabriel Archer stood with Ratcliffe, the others voting that it was imperative to make warehouse space for essential food supplies immediately.

Ratcliffe tried to veto the measure on technical grounds, but the patience of the blunt Newport was exhausted. Everyone, he said, appeared to have forgotten something essential. Under the terms of the charter granted to the sponsors of the colony by King James, the Council was required to elect a new President each year. More than that period had transpired.

Archer obviously hoped to be elected and began to make a speech advocating his candidacy.

Newport cut him short by nominating John Smith.

It was clear to virtually everyone present that Smith deserved the post. He had carried the greatest share of responsibility for the colony's affairs from the outset, had made most of the major decisions and had prevented both starvation and serious mutiny. Thanks to his talents as an organizer, the settlers had survived a harsh winter. He had established cordial relations with the Chickahominy and most of the lesser Indian tribes of the area, and only the Chesapeake and Pamunkey had failed to respond to his gestures of friendship.

The Reverend Hunt, Percy and Martin all clamored for the right to second the nomination, and finally decided to offer a joint endorsement.

The new members of the Council knew the veteran gentlemen-adventurers only slightly, but in the short time they had been in the New World they had been deeply impressed by Smith's dynamic leadership. They joined in the vote for him, and Ratcliffe, hastily trying to make amends, cast his ballot with theirs. Archer was more honest and abstained.

So, in the spring of 1608, Captain John Smith finally won the title to the post he had been holding in all but name.

His acceptance speech was brief. "Gentlemen," he said, "we've learned that America is a land of surprises. But I can promise you one thing. Everyone is going to work as hard as he's able."

IX

FURS AND LUMBER again made up the bulk of the *Susan Constant*'s cargo when she sailed back to England in the late spring of 1608. Captain Newport also carried several kegs of medicinal herbs the settlers had found useful, and he hoped to obtain a high price for them on the London market. Only four of the immigrants decided to return to England, the rest having made up their mind to remain in Jamestown and join the struggle to conquer the forest.

Two passengers of consequence sailed with Newport, and their departure made life much easier for President Smith and his Council colleagues. One was Edward Wingfield, and Smith showed him great compassion. Rather than ruin the man's reputation and make it impossible for him to obtain employment in England, the new President persuaded the Council to drop its charges against his enemy. It was enough, he said, that Wingfield was leaving.

Gabriel Archer went home, too, disgruntled because he truly believed he had deserved the Presidency and been deprived of the post by unfair means. Although it was a relief to be rid of Archer, no one celebrated. He had sworn he intended to persuade the colony's sponsors to uphold his rights, and promised he would return on the *Susan Constant*'s next voyage to Virginia. Everyone who knew him realized he would keep his word, which he did.

At any rate, Smith was now in complete charge of Jamestown, and Ratcliffe was the only one of his persistent foes who remained to badger him. Ten days after Newport's departure another ship was sighted from the Fort, and a few hours later a second vessel sent out by the noble investors cast anchor. She was the *Phoenix*, commanded by Captain Francis Nelson, an old friend of Smith's. On board were sixty more immigrants, one third of them young gentlemen-adventurers. Nelson carried large quantities of supplies, and a new warehouse had to be constructed at once for storage purposes.

Some of the colonists rejoiced, thinking there were now enough provisions on hand to fill the town's needs. But Smith and his Council were worried. In all, as Scrivener wrote, there were now one hundred and twenty newcomers, all of them endowed with hearty appetites, and the supplies on hand would last only a short time if not supplemented by other fare.

The gentlemen-adventurers who had traveled on the *Phoenix* created difficulties from the day they landed. They resented being ordered to work and seemed to think they could spend their time doing what they pleased. They ordered the commoners to prepare their meals, and made the mistake of demanding that some of the veterans evacuate their cottages so they would have comfortable roofs over their heads.

A delegation of the original settlers went to President Smith, who assured them he would handle the situation in his own way. He summoned all the newcomers to the parade ground, and gave them work schedules, which included cutting trees, building houses, standing guard duty, laboring in the fields and attending military drills. The weather was warm, and he said that the new immigrants would sleep in the open until their houses were built.

As he had anticipated, the new gentlemen-adventurers protested violently. Smith calmly informed them that if they wanted to remain in Jamestown, enjoy her protection and eat the food from her stores, they would obey him. If they found the tasks he had outlined distasteful, however, they were free to go out into the forests, make their homes wherever they pleased and find their own food. There was game in the wilderness, he told them, and berries were ripening. Then, very casually, he added that he understood several tribes of savages were on the warpath.

The newcomers looked out at the towering trees of the forest, and not one accepted the President's invitation to leave.

Smith's manner changed. He handed his sword to Percy, and his pistols to Scrivener, both of whom had accompanied him, and offered to settle any differences of opinion with the newcomers in a fist fight. Once again no one accepted.

The following day the immigrants learned still another lesson. Two of the young gentlemen, idlers who had never done a day's work in their lives, were assigned the arduous task of cutting down trees. The unaccustomed labor was exhausting, and they cursed viciously with each swing of their axes.

The incident was duly reported to Smith, and that night he assembled the entire community on the parade ground. The Reverend Hunt delivered a short but incisive sermon on the evils of cursing, and Smith then announced that the two culprits had been guilty of uttering seventy-four oaths. In order to cleanse them, he declared, finding it difficult to keep a straight face, they would be required to pay a penalty for their transgressions. Veteran colonists went to the river for seventy-four bucket loads of water, which were duly dumped over the heads of the sputtering, half-drowned young gentlemen.

Thereafter the newcomers obeyed orders, and no one complained. Veterans and immigrants learned to work side by side, the new arrivals made their first, tentative ventures deep in the forest, and a new era of orderly peace was inaugurated.

When the *Phoenix* sailed for England late in May, 1608, her hold was filled with prime cedar certain to bring a good price in London. Captain Nelson carried with him something even more valuable, the first portion of a book John Smith was writing on the colony's history. Smith had given a great deal of thought to the troubles Jamestown had suffered, and he had concluded that ignorance was responsible for most of them. The financial sponsors of the colony knew literally nothing of the New World and imagined that explorers would find diamonds and emeralds scattered in profusion on the ground. Immigrants who made the voyage to Virginia had literally no concept of the living conditions they would encounter in the New World.

It would be far better, Smith decided, if nobles who made investments in the colony understood what they might gain in return for their money. And Jamestown would become infinitely stronger if the colonists themselves realized what was in store for them. A different class of men would volunteer to settle in Jamestown, and far fewer malcontents would have to be bullied and forced to behave.

Smith had no idea that his book, *A True Relation,* not only would accomplish his goal but would open a new career for him and help win him immortality. It was destined to be the first of eight books he would write, in which he changed England's concepts of the New World and achieved lasting fame.

He knew nothing of his own long-range future, however, as he stood in the tower of the Fort, watching the *Phoenix* sail away. All he realized was that the colony was secure and relatively prosperous for the first time. The crops planted in the spring were ripening in the summer sun. Hunting was good, and fishing parties were returning to Jamestown each day with large catches. Relations with the savages were stable, and Powhatan was being remarkably prompt in his deliveries of food supplies under the new barter agreement.

Equally encouraging was the knowledge that Matthew Scrivener was proving himself an able administrator. He gladly accepted responsibility, performed his duties competently, and had won the respect of the entire community. Smith hesitated to leave Scrivener in charge of affairs at Jamestown by himself, but believed it would be safe to put him in command if Percy and Martin supported and advised him. He discussed the matter with all three, and not only did they accept the idea, but there was no friction among them.

John Smith was free at last to pursue a dream of his own, that of exploring unknown portions of the North American continent.

On June 2, 1608, President Smith left Jamestown in the schooner to explore all of Chesapeake Bay. Accompanying him were a party of thirteen, including six young gentlemen-adventurers, three veteran colonists who had become marksmen, two expert fisherman, a former blacksmith who had prodigious physical strength, and a physician. They carried ample supplies of food, firearms and ammunition, and Smith's personal equipment included quill pens, jars of ink and carefully hoarded supplies of fine, white parchment for map-making. Never had any adventure he had undertaken been more exciting or offered greater promise.

The first stop was made at a small Indian village on the southern shore of the Bay, called Kecoughtan, which was populated by the Chesapeake tribe. The savages were dour, and when they made it obvious that the visitors were not welcome, Smith and his companions departed at once. Smith, usually so sensitive to subtleties, saw nothing particularly significant in the attitude of the Indians, and apparently did not realize there might be difficulties ahead in Jamestown's relations with the Chesapeake, who deeply resented the invasion of their territory by foreigners.

Near the eastern shore of the bay the party found a group of islands, which were named after Smith. They are among the

very few of his discoveries bearing his name; in spite of his
alleged vanity, he did not follow the example set by most
explorers of his age, who named large bodies of water and
land after themselves.

The voyagers next encountered the savages of the Accow-
mack tribe, and Smith was delighted to discover they spoke the
language of the Chickahominy, which made it easy for him to
establish friendly relations with them. One of the most valuable
of the services he performed for future generations on this voyage of discovery was his careful pinpointing, on maps, of the
precise locations of the Indian nations of the area. Settlers who
came to Chesapeake Bay over the course of the next one hundred years had reason to be grateful to him.

Two summer squalls that broke in quick succession on the
same day almost forced the travelers to abandon their enterprise.
The rain was torrential, accompanied by lightning and thunder,
the bay kicked up high waves, and the frail little schooner's
foremast broke off and was washed over the side. The craft
began to leak, too, and was kept afloat only by frantic bailing.
But no one thought of turning back. A new mast was made
by chopping down a suitable tree, and the damaged foresail
was repaired with material from the men's shirts.

The cruise continued, with the explorers going ashore every
few hours, and Smith noted that there were wolves, bears, deer
and a variety of smaller animals in this part of the wilderness.
He made careful notes on the great abundance of game here,
thinking that it might be useful for hunters to visit the region
in the event of future food shortages at Jamestown.

What started as a pleasant voyage became hard labor. The
winds died down completely, and the men had to use the
schooner's oars, spending the better part of each day rowing the

little vesser. Exhaustion made them careless, they frequently splashed water onto the deck, and their bread became soaked with sea water. Some wanted to return to Jamestown, but Smith would not listen to such talk. He placed the bread on the tops of barrels, where it would dry in the sun, and told his companions it would be disgraceful to turn back when they still carried a full month's provisions.

The muttering subsided, in part because the men's spirits improved after Smith lectured them, in part because they were afraid of arousing the President's anger. Like so many natural leaders, John Smith had an instinct for handling subordinates, and not once during his long, eventful stay in the New World was he unable to deal effectively with dissension or potential mutiny.

On June 16 the party reached the mouth of a river eight or nine miles wide, and Smith was elated. Perhaps, as his friend Henry Hudson hoped, the stream led to the Pacific Ocean. He began to travel up its length, and sailed approximately thirty miles before encountering other human beings. Suddenly a large band of warriors appeared from the forest and sent a shower of arrows in the direction of the schooner. Smith responded at once by ordering the men to fire their muskets in the air, and the savages were so awed by the firesticks that they threw down their arms and made friendly overtures.

The explorers learned that the braves were members of the Potomac nation and that their river bore the same name. So John Smith won the honor of discovering the great river on which, almost two hundred years later, the capital of the United States of America would be built.

Once again careful notes were made of the wildlife in the vicinity. Otter, beaver and sable dwelled in the forest, and the

waters of the river were thick with fish. If the party had carried
nets, thousands would have been landed, Smith wrote. But the
explorers were forced to improvise, and hauled scores of fish
onto the deck with kettles, buckets—and a frying pan. Smith
devised an ingenious method of catching fish, spearing many of
them with his sword.

The Potomac Indians, who spoke a dialect Smith was able
to make out, with some difficulty, told him of a mine near one
of their villages. This was the first mention by any savages of
the possible presence of precious metals or gems in the region,
and Smith immediately went off to investigate, accompanied
by two of the young gentlemen-adventurers. They marched for
approximately ten miles through a part of the forest infested
with gnats, flies and mosquitos, and at last came to a shallow
surface mine the natives had dug.

It proved almost worthless, however, and yielded nothing except a few traces of low-grade iron ore. Twenty-four hours were
spent in a careful, exhaustive search of the immediate surround-
ings, but no other signs of metal were discovered. Smith now
believed, more firmly than ever, that the stories of gold, silver
and diamonds on the eastern seaboard of North America were
products of greedy men's imaginations.

The three Englishmen returned to the schooner, where they
and the rest of the party amused themselves by catching more
fish. From the savages' description of the river it had become
plain that the Potomac did not have an outlet in the Pacific, so
Smith decided to return to Chesapeake Bay after a day of rest
and sport.

The seemingly harmless pastime of catching fish almost
proved fatal to him, however. While he was spearing fish his
hand and arm occasionally plunged beneath the surface of the

water, and at one point, while they were immersed, he was stung by an ugly creature with long tentacles. His arm immediately began to swell, and within a few minutes appeared two or three times its normal size.

Everyone, including Smith himself, thought he would die, and the young gentlemen-adventurers immediately hoisted sail for a rapid return to Jamestown. Smith's pain was excruciating, and he was out of his mind for approximately twenty-four hours. The party's physician was uncertain how to treat the wound, but finally decided to lance it with a long, needle-like instrument. Smith bled freely, the swelling was reduced, and the physician anointed the injured hand with what was called "a precious oil."

President Smith regained his senses, and although somewhat weakened, was anxious to resume the voyage. He decided, however, that it would not be amiss to return briefly to Jamestown. He was dissatisfied with the attitude of some of his companions, whom he intended to replace, and preferred to take a fresh supply of provisions on board before continuing with his explorations.

The schooner reached Jamestown on July 21, and, as usual, there were problems to be settled. Ratcliffe had insisted on building himself a new, splendid house of oak and cedar and had commandeered the services of eleven men to help him. Scrivener had been unable to control the former President and had been forced to let Ratcliffe do as he pleased.

Smith took charge and was not surprised to discover that Ratcliffe, who had obtained possession of one of the keys to the new warehouse, had hidden considerable quantities of stolen provisions in the house. The food was immediately returned, the key was given to Scrivener, and the house, which was large enough to accommodate at least ten men, was turned over to some of the new immigrants. The seething Ratcliffe was forced to return to his former cottage.

Some of the new members of the community were ill, probably as a result of drinking water from a stagnant pond in the forest. The physician gave them an "elixir" made of powdered wilderness herbs, and they showed a dramatic improvement. Most were able to return to their work by the following day.

Fresh provisions were loaded on the schooner, and on July 24, after spending only three days at Jamestown, Smith set sail again. He had replaced one of the gentlemen-adventurers and three of the commoners in the party.

For some days the voyage was uneventful, and only one minor incident was worthy of Smith's mention in the account he later wrote about the expedition. Near the mouth of the Potomac, while the schooner was anchored for the night, eight large war canoes filled with braves of the Massawomeke nation paddled toward the vessel. Afraid their intentions were hostile and that they might attack if they realized how few Englishmen were traveling in the schooner, Smith resorted to a simple but effective trick.

The men put their hats and helmets on sticks and distributed themselves among these dummy figures. Then, when they brandished their muskets, the savages, who were not able to make them out too clearly in the dark, thought there was a large party on board the vessel. The braves became panicky and paddled away. They did not molest the Englishmen again.

At the northeastern end of Chesapeake Bay the party encountered another group of natives, who proved to be members of a very large and powerful nation called the Susquehanna. The warriors were pleased when they found they could under-

stand Smith, who spoke to them in the tongue of the Chickahominy, and that he could make out what they were saying.
They told him that one of their main towns was located some
distance up a mighty river whose mouth was a short distance
away.

Smith was intrigued, again thinking of finding a water route
across North America to the Pacific. But he had no intention of
offending a powerful tribe by sailing unbidden into its territory. He sent the braves with gifts to their sachem and elders,
requesting that they meet him at the mouth of the river.

He waited four days at the mouth of the great Susquehanna
River, and at last a party of sixty warriors accompanied their
sachem to the rendezvous, bringing with them gifts in return,
including venison, tobacco and the first buffalo meat the Englishmen had ever tasted. Relations were so cordial that the
savages invited their guests to accompany them up the river,
which they did, and the explorers spent several days at the town
of the Susquehanna.

These natives, who were by far the tallest and most powerfully built savages the Jamestown settlers had yet encountered,
lived in houses of stone, had made a gristmill for corn by har-
nessing the waters of the river and, in general, seemed the most
advanced of the North American tribes. They owned several
axes of steel that were obviously of European make, and in
reply to Smith's questioning they revealed they had been visited
on several occasions by parties of French explorers from Canada.
They had not really trusted these foreigners, however, and as
they considered their river sacred, they had kept the Frenchmen some distance from it, not permitting them to see it or even
admitting its presence.

Therefore John Smith achieved the additional honor of being the first civilized man to discover another major river of the eastern seaboard of North America, the Susquehanna. He learned from the savages that it became increasingly narrow farther inland and that its headwaters were located in mountains to the west. So his hope of finding a water route to the Pacific vanished again, but he made an additional two days' journey up the river with a small party of warriors, who were fascinated by the painstakingly accurate maps he drew of their river and the surrounding countryside in the region that would later become Pennsylvania.

The Englishmen then returned to Chesapeake Bay and headed toward Jamestown, exploring the western shores. Smith added two more rivers to his growing list of discoveries, the Rappahannock and the Patuxent, both of which he mapped. Sudden tragedy marred the voyage when one of the young gentlemen-adventurers, Richard Fetherstone, became ill and, a few hours later, died. He was buried with full military honors, a cross was placed over his grave and Smith, who always carried his Bible with him, read a prayer.

The next day the explorers were attacked by the Chesapeake, the most consistently antagonistic of the Indians. One of the men sustained an arrow wound in the thigh, but his wound was dressed by the physician. The savages were driven off by musket fire, and at least one warrior was killed. Now the Chesapeake had a real score to settle.

Another squall blew up near the southern end of Chesapeake Bay and was so violent that everyone in the party had to bail water for all of an afternoon and night. The wind and sea were so ferocious that even the perennially optimistic Smith thought it likely the schooner would break up before morning. But when the storm subsided at dawn the battered craft was still intact and the men were safe.

Smith held a short prayer service of thanksgiving, and then made a proposal that startled his weary companions. Their task was not yet complete, he told them. They had visited all of Chesapeake Bay except the southern end, and he suggested they complete their explorations, particularly as they would be visiting a region close to home. The tired men had been hoping to reach Jamestown that same day and go straight to bed, but the President managed to fire them with his own enthusiasm, and they agreed to prolong the voyage.

They sailed approximately fifteen miles up the stream that in time would become known as the Elizabeth River, and saw no sign of any living creature. Finally they came to an Indian village that looked as though it had just been abandoned. Smith knew this was the land of the Pamunkey, who had consistently refused the settlers' friendship, and, feeling uneasy, he decided it might be unwise to go farther inland.

The explorers sailed down the river again, and as they neared its mouth they were greeted by a crossfire of arrows from both banks. They had allowed themselves to be ambushed, and when they recovered from their initial surprise they saw war canoes half-hidden in the tall reeds on both sides of the river.

Smith still hoped it might be possible to establish a rapport with neighbors who lived so close to Jamestown. Knowing the Pamunkey understood the language of the Chickahominy, he called out to the warriors, offering them peace and trade. They replied with another barrage of arrows, one of which passed through the sleeve of a gentleman-adventurer. When another cut into the crown of the physician's hat, Smith realized he could afford to be tolerant no longer. He ordered the muskets fired simultaneously at both banks, and the savages fled in such haste that they abandoned their canoes as they jumped ashore. Many left behind their bows, arrows and other equipment, and the coldly angry Smith decided to teach them a lesson. When he felt it necessary he could be merciless, and he did not hesitate now. Driving first toward one bank, then the other, he and his men chopped the war canoes to kindling with their axes. They deliberately destroyed the warriors' weapons and, suspecting the braves were watching them from the sanctuary of the dark forest, cut to ribbons the belts of seashell-encrusted leather that all the Indians of the area considered sacred good luck charms.

One of the leaders of the Pamunkey called out to the Englishmen, offering them baskets of corn if they would stop. But Smith refused to be bribed, just as he had rejected intimidation, and the settlers did not halt until all of the canoes and their contents were smashed. Then Smith cupped his hands and shouted to the Pamunkey. If they wanted peace, he declared, they could have it by coming to Jamestown, where he would guarantee their safety and present them with gifts. But if they preferred war, he would destroy them.

There was no reply from the forest, and the explorers started toward Jamestown on the last stage of their voyage. Later Smith was criticized by his foes, who claimed he had treated the Pamunkey too harshly and had lost a chance to win their friendship. His reply was curt. In his opinion, he said, the situation required a show of firmness, and he did what he thought best. Had he accepted the bribe, the savages would have awaited another opportunity to attack the settlers. His demonstration of strength, he believed, was the only language the warriors really understood.

In any event, the schooner reached Jamestown safely on September 7, 1608. The entire voyage, interrupted for three days in July, had occupied virtually the entire summer, and would be remembered for all time as an epic journey. The maps of Chesapeake Bay and the rivers feeding into it—made by a man who had never received formal training in art work of any kind—were such marvels of accuracy they were used for more than two hundred years by mariners, settlers, traders and military men. America owed Smith a permanent debt that never could be repaid.

X

ANY FEELING OF TRIUMPH John Smith felt after his successful voyage of exploration vanished when he returned to Jamestown and resumed the complex burdens of his office as President. The roof of the new warehouse had leaked during his absence, and heavy rains had spoiled some of the food supplies brought to the colony on the *Phoenix.* Two of the gentlemen-adventurers had fought a duel, which was against the law, and were in jail until the President could decide what to do with them. Two of the new immigrants had been killed in an accident, and three others had died after contracting the same mysterious illness that had afflicted so many of the original settlers. Spirits were so low that the colonists were being lax in harvesting their crops, which were ripe. And former president Ratcliffe was in jail, on orders of the Council, charged with trying to incite a mutiny.

Smith took command at once with his customary brisk efficiency. He ordered a new warehouse roof built immediately, and put the entire community to work harvesting crops. He interviewed the duelists, heard their stories and then signed a decree deporting them on the next ship that put into the port. His treatment of Ratcliffe was lenient, however. Even though the man had been a disturbing influence ever since they had left England almost two years earlier, Smith felt sorry for him. Believing that Ratcliffe could do no real harm while he himself was in Jamestown, he gave the troublemaker a pardon.

His cure for the low spirits of the colonists was swift. As soon as all other tasks were completed he put them to work building houses for the next shipload of immigrants, who were due to arrive at any time. Additional fields were cleared and prepared for the following spring's planting. Hunting and fishing duties were increased, and military training, which had tapered off during his absence, was resumed. Busy men, he told the Council, had little time to brood or worry about their health.

A month later, in October, the *Susan Constant* reached Jamestown for the third time. The faithful Captain Newport had loaded her with provisions and other supplies, and she brought seventy passengers, among them two new members of the Council, Peter Winne and Richard Waldo, and one former member, the perennial troublemaker, Gabriel Archer.

Some of the newcomers were Dutch, and a number of others were Poles. Their arrival set a precedent, since they were the first non-English settlers. They had been persuaded to make the voyage by the colony's sponsors, who directed President Smith to put them to work "in some enterprise that will show a handsome profit, most preferably the making of glass."

An even more significant precedent was shattered by the arrival of two women. The moment they stepped ashore Jamestown was no longer an all-male community. One was the wife of Thomas Forest, a young gentleman-adventurer, and literally nothing is known about her, not even her first name. The other was Anne Burrowes, her maidservant, who later married one of the original settlers, John Laydon.

The presence of the two women marked the beginning of a new era in Virginia. The mere fact that they had been permitted to make the voyage meant that Smith, Newport and the Council considered the colony a relatively safe and permanent place. Now married men could send for their families, and bachelors had reason to hope that boatloads of single women whom they could marry would start arriving soon.

Captain Newport, the immigrants and the fresh supplies were welcome, but a letter from the sponsors soured Smith and made him wonder if the noble investors had lost their sanity. In spite of all that he and Newport had told the lords about conditions in the New World, their chief aim was still that of obtaining a quick fortune. The President was directed by his superiors to make the finding of gold, silver, emeralds and diamonds his first order of business, even if it should become necessary to neglect other phases of the colony's life.

Smith was in despair, and Newport sympathized with him. It was the President's duty to obey the sponsors, who held a patent from King James and therefore spoke in the name of the crown. But the conditions they had outlined might destroy Jamestown. Not only were they apparently incapable of realizing that there were no precious metals and gems in Virginia, but they shortsightedly failed to recognize the basic facts of wilderness conditions. Any failure to obtain food from all available sources could lead to the starvation of the growing settlement. And neglect of the colony's defenses would permit the Pamunkey or Chesapeake to slaughter the inhabitants.

It had been John Smith's aim, ever since first landing in Virginia, to make the colony self-sufficient. His policy of concentrating on the planting of corn and other cereals, augmented by vegetables, was at last paying dividends, as was his strict scheduling of hunting and fishing parties. The arrival of another large group of immigrants meant it would be necessary to keep trading with the Indians in order to obtain additional provisions, but he was making great progress in moving toward his goal.

It would be criminal, he told Newport, to take men from vital tasks and send them on fools' errands.

He was equally disturbed by the sponsors' bland statement that military activities were a waste of time. They sent the President a crown, ordering him to present it to Powhatan in the name of King James, and they calmly asserted that this gift would guarantee the pacification of the Indians, who would then become English vassals.

"If Powhatan had any idea the nobles have made King James his overlord," Smith said to Newport, "the sachem would have all our scalps. And I wonder how they think we're going to make peace with the Chesapeake and Pamunkey. Certainly the gift of this crown to Powhatan won't do it! And now that I think of it, the base of this ridiculous crown is made of pewter. It will tarnish, and Powhatan may become very angry."

Regardless of his own feelings and common sense aims, he had to obey the investors, so he prepared for a new mission to the interior. Newport went with him, and the company consisted of twenty men and two boys, Ned and Thaddeus. The town of the Chickahominy was the party's first stop, and there Powhatan was presented with the crown.

The sachem was not fooled by the gift, nor did it please him. Fortunately, Smith's embarrassment was so evident in presenting it to him that Powhatan did not bear a grudge against him or Jamestown itself. He began to understand, however, that many men of stature in England were not as wise as Smith and Newport.

Powhatan was rather reluctant to let the settlers roam where they pleased through his realm, and was puzzled by the explanation that they were required to search for gold and jewels. He had heard of neither, and didn't know what they meant. So Smith proposed that Thaddeus and Ned remain in the Chickahominy town as hostages guaranteeing the colonists' good intentions, and that Opachisco and a company of warriors accompany the expedition.

The suggestions were so fair that Powhatan immediately accepted them. The two boys spent several weeks with the Chickahominy, and devoted hours each day to talks with Pocahontas, who had a fresh opportunity to perfect her English. She was able to read and speak the language easily now, and she told the boys her great, private secret: the Bible had so impressed her that she intended to become a Christian whenever the opportunity arose.

Opachisco and his braves conducted the settlers on a long march of exploration through the interior of Virginia. The Englishmen, all of them members of the original colony, were so accustomed to the wilderness that they felt completely at home in the forest and were able to live as comfortably as the savages. Smith mentioned their ability to adapt to the New World in his final chapters of *A True Relation,* and had the foresight to declare that what one band of immigrants had done, others could do. The day would come, he declared, when all who traveled to the New World would make themselves at home there.

Precisely as the leaders of the expedition had anticipated, no traces of gems or precious metals were found anywhere. Smith prepared maps of the region, however, which would prove as valuable to future generations of colonists arriving in Virginia as the discovery of a gold mine. He was more than a trailblazer; he turned on the floodlights that enabled newcomers to find their way in the limitless forest.

The explorers spent about a month in the forest and returned to Jamestown by way of the Chickahominy town, where Ned and Thaddeus rejoined them. In the strict sense the London-inspired mission had been a failure. The noble patent holders would continue to earn a modest profit on their investment, with no chance of acquiring the vast wealth that had led them to invest in the enterprise. Many years would pass before John Smith's maps and acutely sensitive descriptions of Virginia would be fully recognized and appreciated by more than a small handful of men. For the present, only the frequent intercession of Prince Henry and Archdeacon Hakluyt with the other sponsors made it possible for him to govern the colony according to his own sound ideas, principles which were helping Jamestown survive and grow.

The frustrated gold-seekers returned to the settlement, where Scrivener reported rising tensions between Englishmen on the one hand and the Dutch and Poles on the other. Smith was outraged. The mere fact that bad feeling existed because of differences in men's origins was a violation of the fundamentals that he believed to be the greatest strength of the unique colonial experiment.

He called the entire community to a special meeting, where the Reverend Hunt read passages from Scriptures on the brotherhood of man. Then President Smith delivered a short, pungent sermon. The wilderness, he said, could not distinguish between gentleman and commoner, Englishman and alien. In the forest all men were equal and either worked together for the common good or perished. Experience had proved there was no alternative, and no man could be exempted. Those who violated the spirit of equality were harmful influences, capable of damaging the united efforts of everyone else. Such influences would be removed.

"No one is better than anyone else because of birth or nationality," he declared. "If the well-born believe themselves superior to the lowly, let them prove it in the forest. I've often found the contrary to be true. Is one who speaks English the master of one who speaks a foreign language? All of us are foreigners here, and we must make our new home together, or the wilderness will punish us. Each of us has the same chance to prove himself strong or weak, resourceful or inept, courageous or cowardly. We have but one goal. Let us strive toward it together."

Anyone who violated the principle of equality, he insisted, would injure the whole colony and therefore would be deported. But he hoped it would be unnecessary to deal harshly with any man. "We have the chance to make this world new in more than name, as different from the old order as these virgin forests are unlike the cities of England and Europe. Together we can make this a shining land, not only for ourselves, but for those who will come here after us."

In the weeks prior to the departure of the *Susan Constant,* while the colonists were preparing a cargo of glass, pitch, lumber and tar, Smith and Newport had their first real dispute. The sailors, who lived on board the ship, ate their own provisions and were burdened with few responsibilities while in port, were disrupting Jamestown's relations with the savages. Some of the seamen bartered portions of their daily food rations with the Indians, and others traded their own knives and axes for furs.

Smith insisted that these activities be stopped, since they were interfering with the barter scale he had worked out with the natives. Newport, who was usually farsighted and sensible, came to the defense of his men and refused to curtail their activities. Smith countered by saying he was being given no choice. For the good of the whole colony he would have to utilize his powers as President and order the crew of the *Susan Constant* not to come ashore. He proved he meant business by sending Percy to the ship with twenty militiamen, who were armed with loaded muskets. For a day and a night the seamen were forcibly detained on the vessel.

Newport realized he had been beaten. On board the *Susan Constant* his word was absolute, and he was forced to recognize the principle that, no matter what his own views, in Jamestown he had to accept another's judgment and authority. He accepted his defeat with good grace, and his friendship with Smith survived the dispute. Neither man was petty, and both proved their generosity of spirit by forgetting their differences.

When Newport sailed back to England in November, 1608, he carried with him the last portion of the manuscript of *A True Relation.* The book was published soon after his arrival in England, creating something of a sensation. It was read, avidly, by people in many walks of life, and undoubtedly became a factor in persuading men of solid worth to immigrate to the New World. But the gold fever was still so intense that Jamestown would be forced to undergo still more tribulations before people in England really gained a clear understanding of conditions in North America.

Newport also carried Smith's maps to England. They were published in a separate volume, together with his descriptions of the country, its wildlife, trees and plants. One section was devoted to the Indian tribes and their customs. This book did not enjoy a popular sale, but was even more influential than *A True Relation,* as it was read by scientists, scholars and university professors at Oxford and Cambridge, as well as by some of the greatest nobles in the realm and by wealthy merchants who were becoming interested in financing New World settlements. All these men of substance gained a far better understanding of America by reading Smith's work.

Among those who, in time, paid a great deal of attention to Smith's books were the members of the Separatist religious sect exiled by King James and living in Holland. Thanks to the work of John Smith, the Separatists, known as the Pilgrims, sailed to America in 1620 on board the *Mayflower* and established their own colony in the wilderness.

Newport also carried copies of Smith's maps to Henry Hudson, who received them a few weeks before he left England for Amsterdam, where he was employed by the Dutch to seek a sea passage to the Orient. Hudson had Smith's maps in his possession when he made his own epic voyage of New World discovery in 1609 on board a little ship called the *Half Moon.* It was on this journey that he discovered the site of what later became New York City, found the river subsequently called the Hudson and sailed upstream as far as an Indian village that, in time, was to become Albany. Smith's influence on others who explored and settled North America can scarcely be measured.

Captain Newport carried one more document with him, a blistering letter that President Smith sent to the noble patent holders. In no mood for nonsense, he criticized the quality of the colonists sent to Jamestown up to that time, saying that great efforts had to be expended to make these men behave and turn them into useful citizens. In the future, he declared bluntly, he preferred honest and competent carpenters, masons, farmers, gardeners and fishermen. And, once again, he told the lords to forget their dreams of acquiring great, unearned wealth.

Smith felt no real confidence in his ability to persuade the investors to adopt a new attitude. But he continued to hope they would become more realistic in their demands. He learned from Newport that Edward Wingfield, who had made a personal report to the nobles, had shown surprising tact, in part because he had not wanted to sully his own name. In any event, Wingfield had substantiated, in essence, all that Smith and Newport had been saying about the potential of America. So, perhaps, the combined weight of evidence presented by men who had actually spent time in Virginia would be effective.

But it was difficult, in frontier Jamestown, to feel tolerant and make excuses for men living in London's comfort. The problems of the wilderness were still pressing, and the colony's situation was still precarious. More than two hundred people were living behind the sheltering palisade wall now, and although their houses were snug and dry, the increase in population had been so sharp that the need for provisions remained critical.

"There was never a time," President Smith wrote in later years, "that we were free of the fear of starvation."

It was true that the storehouse and the new warehouse were filled with the produce of the colonists themselves, the supplies sent from England and the meat and corn obtained from the savages. But Smith, Scrivener and the Council did some simple arithmetic, and knew that, even with strict rationing, there would be nothing left by mid-February unless additional food was obtained elsewhere.

There was only one place to turn. Smith had to increase the volume of trade with the Indians, but he knew he had to use great caution. The warriors were becoming insistent in their demand for firearms, which he was determined to keep out of their hands at all costs. He knew the hostile tribes would become bolder if they gained possession of muskets, and even the Indian nations with whom good relations had been established might turn against the Englishmen if they felt themselves on equal military terms.

Although needing food supplies from the natives, Smith realized he had to exercise great caution in making his wants known. Jamestown had become sufficiently large to cause even the Chickahominy to feel that the intruders were threatening their preserves. So the problem now was that of obtaining enough provisions for a growing community without letting the Indians know they had the power, if they refused to barter, to starve out the settlers.

Scrivener and Percy were the most efficient of Smith's assistants, and he sent them into the interior on separate missions. Each was accompanied by a small militia escort, and both groups carried large quantities of the goods the savages admired and wanted. But neither of the deputies had learned the language of the Indians sufficiently well to handle the chiefs of the tribes. Both parties returned with disappointingly small quantities of food.

It was difficult for Smith to leave Jamestown for a long period when the administration of the community took up so much of his time. So he wrote a letter to Powhatan in English, requesting Pocahontas to translate it for her father. The sachem sent back a shrewd reply. He would give the colonists all the corn and venison they needed, he declared, on two conditions. He demanded a grindstone as a gift, and he wanted a company of Englishmen to build him a house as handsome and sturdy as the buildings in Jamestown.

Smith had no choice, and twenty-four men responded to his call for volunteers. They set out for the town of the Chickahominy immediately after Christmas, and spent two weeks erecting the house. Since Smith had not accompanied the expedition himself, the Chickahominy warriors felt free to steal from the settlers, and took tools, two or three bags of gunpowder and several muskets. The settlers demanded the return of their property, but the natives pretended not to understand them, and when the colonists issued harsh threats, it appeared that a battle might develop a any time. A messenger was sent off to Jamestown to acquaint Smith with the situation.

The President was alarmed. It was essential to the safety of Jamestown to avoid a war with the powerful Chickahominy. But, at the same time, it was equally important that the property be recovered and the thieves punished. He knew that if he ignored the incident, every brave in Virginia would be tempted to steal from the settlers. So he set out at once for the town of the Chickahominy, accompanied only by a young gentleman-adventurer, John Russell. Scrivener was left in charge at Jamestown.

What Smith did not know was that Scrivener had changed. Like so many who had preceded him on the Council, he had become highly ambitious in his own right. Friends in England had written to him, indicating they expected him to become President in the near future. And Gabriel Archer, still jealous of Smith, insidiously played on the vanity of the man to whom Smith had given so much responsibility.

"You're doing all the work," Archer told Scrivener, "and Smith takes all the credit. Stand up for your own rights. Prepare the ground and be ready to take over. Win the support of the colonists, and they'll turn Smith out of office, just as they turned out Wingfield."

Scrivener listened to the foolish advice and, in order to make himself more popular, increased the settlers' food rations during the President's absence. Many of the new arrivals, unable to see beyond the immediate present, were delighted, but the veteran colonists were deeply concerned. They knew the meaning of starvation, and were afraid the precious food stocks would be depleted before spring.

With a dangerous situation festering at home, Smith was facing critical problems at the town of the Chickahominy. Powhatan at first denied that any of his warriors could have stolen from the settlers, and became indignant. But when Smith refused to be bullied, the sachem changed his story, and flatly declared that if any of the colonists' property had been taken, he knew nothing about it.

President Smith realized that if he called Powhatan a liar to his face, the head of the Indian confederation would feel compelled to break off relations with the Englishmen and go to war in order to salvage his honor. So, treading delicately, Smith suggested that the Chickahominy be informed that no one would be punished and the incident would be closed if the stolen goods were returned. He suggested that the property be placed in front of the house that the settlers were building for Powhatan, and that the items be returned late at night, when everyone was sleeping. In that way, the precise identity of the culprits would never be known.

Powhatan seemed amenable. His warriors were duly told of the plan and informed that the thieves should return the property that same night.

Smith, trying as always to be scrupulously fair, kept no watch that night. He thought he had handled the explosive situation with great tact and told young Russell he confidently expected the tools and weapons would be found the following morning in front of the partly built house.

But when morning came, there were no tools or weapons to be seen. Smith went at once to Powhatan, and was shocked to discover that the sachem and his entire family were absent. A brave who had been designated to act as his sachem's spokesman muttered a flimsy excuse to the effect that Powhatan had been called away to another of the Chickahominy towns, deeper in the interior.

Smith's first thought was that Powhatan had vanished because he felt ashamed to face his guest. But the morning wore on and the English and Dutch settlers, keeping to their bargain, continued to work on the house. Braves gathered in small groups to stare at the foreigners and speak to one another in undertones. Whenever Smith appeared, the savages promptly scattered.

Something strange was happening, and the atmosphere became increasingly tense. Smith couldn't help wondering if there had been some sinister reason for Powhatan's sudden disappearance.

XI

THE STORM BROKE shortly before noon. Smith, accompanied by Russell, had climbed to the roof of the unfinished house to inspect the progress of the work. He had been seeking answers to the questions that pressed on his mind but had found none. All he knew was that something had to be done, or the Chickahominy would lose all respect for the Jamestown settlers. If that should happen, the colony would never again be safe from the threat of a massive attack.

While Smith and the young gentleman-adventurer made their inspection, the colonists returned to the ground for their noon meal, going off in twos and threes for a quiet time of rest and relaxation. There were no Chickahominy anywhere in the immediate vicinity, but neither Smith nor Russell noticed that the Indians had absented themselves.

Suddenly, as the two men were climbing down a ladder to the ground, thirty or forty warriors burst into the clearing, shouting and brandishing spears, knives and clubs.

Had the English and Dutch workmen rallied to Smith's side, the attack could have been beaten off with ease. But the colonists became panicky and scattered. Smith and Russell were left to face the savage mob alone, and too late Smith knew that Powhatan had gone away in order not to associate himself with the assault.

Both men drew their pistols, and Smith urged his companion

to take careful aim, wasting no shots. They waited until the braves drew closer, then fired. Both of Smith's shots were excellent, and he killed a warrior with each. Russell proved almost as good a marksman, killing one brave and wounding another.

Apparently the savages had anticipated casualties, and this time the sound of firearms did not have its customary effect. The warriors did not falter, and continued to rush toward the two Englishmen. One of the braves in command of the group called something unintelligible, and the savages promptly spread out to encircle the pair.

Smith devised the best possible tactics to deal with the critical situation. Aware that he could not rely on help from the settlers who had scurried away, he managed to tell Russell, above the uproar, that they should stand back to back. They did, and as there was no time to reload their pistols, they jammed the useless weapons into their belts and drew their swords.

When the Chickahominy realized that firearms would not be used against them again, they took heart, and their drive became still more ferocious. Dancing, capering and screaming, they completely surrounded the two Englishmen.

What they did not know and therefore could not take into account was that John Smith's sword was as deadly a weapon as a pistol. A tall warrior leaped toward him, club raised high, and Smith, with a thrust so deft it seemed effortless, disposed of the Indian. Russell was an accomplished swordsman, too, and although not in Smith's class, was sufficiently competent to give the foes pressing in on him reason to become somewhat more cautious.

The beleaguered pair thrust and slashed, cutting and, when necessary, parrying spear thrusts with steel. Smith was unrelenting. Not content to drive off the savages, he was determined to make them pay as great a penalty as he could, and in the next quarter of an hour he lost count of the warriors he killed or wounded. Russell was almost his equal, and eventually the two men wreaked such havoc that the Chickahominy withdrew and vanished into the forest.

The brief battle became renowned as one of the truly epic struggles of the early American frontier. Smith and Russell, who were unharmed, had killed seven warriors and wounded nine.

The aroused Smith called to the workmen in a loud voice, and the English and Dutch settlers, sheepishly ashamed of their cowardice, came to him from the woods in which they had taken refuge. When all of them had gathered he made a very short, blistering speech, in which he said he would give them a chance to redeem themselves.

They made certain that muskets were loaded and primed. Smith and Russell then reloaded their pistols, and the grim company marched cautiously from the heights on which the house was being built into the Chickahominy town.

The few elders and squaws in sight hastily withdrew into their huts. No children were to be seen anywhere, and the braves were conspicuously absent.

Smith marched his men to the longhouse of the young warriors and set it on fire with a little gunpowder, which they sparked with a tinderbox and flint. While it burned and flames leaped up toward the sky, Smith sent Russell with several men to bring two of the elders to him.

The old Indians thought he was going to kill them and faced him with remarkable calm.

"Find the warriors of the Chickahominy," he told them sternly, "and tell them to return to their home. Send a runner to Powhatan, sachem of the Chickahominy. No matter where he is hiding, find him. Tell him to return to his home. All must be assembled this day, before the sun sets. If they are not, the strangers-from-across-the-sea will burn the whole town of the Chickahominy to the ground. Only ashes will remain."

The elders were released, and went off into the forest. Hours passed, and there was no sign of the braves, which was more or less what Smith had expected. He had believed they would wait for Powhatan and return with him, provided the sachem accepted the ultimatum. If Powhatan remained defiant and stayed away, however, it would be necessary to carry out the threat and burn the town of the Chickahominy. If the colonists perpetrated such an act, there would be no chance to avert a full-scale war with the largest Indian nation in Virginia, but Smith was convinced he had no choice. The unprovoked attempt on his life, coupled with the stealing of weapons and tools, could not go unchallenged. A failure to retaliate would doom Jamestown.

Smith moved his company to a cleared field on the heights above the Chickahominy town, where it would be impossible for the Indians to launch a surprise attack from the shelter of the forest. There each settler placed his ammunition and gunpowder beside him, so he could reload his musket in the shortest time possible. The wait was interminable, and tension increased as the day wore on. Smith was determined to burn the town if his conditions were not met, and several of his men, watched from below by squaws and elders, collected brushwood, which they fashioned into torches.

Suddenly, about an hour before sundown, Powhatan emerged alone from the forest. A majestic, solemn figure in his feathered cape, he carried no weapons, and it would have been easy, when he halted, for a marksman to kill him with a musket shot. The sachem knew it, but was proving that he, like Smith, was willing to take risks.

He gestured, and his subjects swarmed into the open. First came his own family, led by Opachisco. Smith caught a quick glimpse of Pocahontas before she turned away with the women, and saw that she had been weeping. Obviously she was desperately unhappy.

Senior warriors and younger braves by the hundreds moved into the clearing, but made no attempt to follow the sachem as he walked, slowly and alone, toward the hill.

Smith went part of the way down the slope to meet him, telling Russell to open a musket barrage at the first sign of treachery.

The President-Governor of Jamestown and the leader of the Chickahominy greeted each other stiffly. Accusations were unnecessary, and Smith waited for Powhatan to speak.

The sachem surprised him by apologizing with grace and warmth. The attempt to kill Smith had been unwarranted and unauthorized, Powhatan said. It had been planned by three warriors, one of whom Smith had killed. The other two had been executed the moment Powhatan had learned of the assault.

Smith inclined his head, but made no reply. He found it impossible to believe the glib story. But as Powhatan was at least going through the motions of punishing the allegedly guilty, he thought it wise to wait.

The other warriors who had taken part in the attack, the sachem continued, had been banished to a remote village in the interior, and would be compelled to remain there for a year. Their disgrace, according to Indian standards, was severe.

The sachem beckoned, and two braves came forward with

the settlers' missing tools and muskets. The men responsible, Powhatan said, had been made to run a gantlet. Apologizing again, he said he wanted to make amends by offering the colonists large quantities of venison and corn as a gift.

Smith felt reasonably certain he would never learn the full, true story of what had happened. He believed that Powhatan had known in advance of the attempted murder and had at least condoned the effort. But the peace was so precarious he swallowed his own anger for the sake of Jamestown's good. By going through the motions of accepting at face value all the sachem had said, he could maintain a delicate truce.

Refusing to apologize for the burning of the longhouse, a symbol of his intention to fight back against aggression, he accepted the corn and venison. But, he said, he would not take the food as a gift. Jamestown preferred to pay its own way and wanted no favors from anyone.

That night the settlers slept in the unfinished house, maintaining a strong watch, and the next morning two of the colonists were sent off to the coast for knives and cooking utensils to be used in trade for the additional provisions. Smith insisted on keeping his word, and work on the house was resumed, with the settlers keeping their weapons close at hand. Smith remained to see the task through to the end. He believed he was needed in Jamestown, but thought it more important that he stay.

A few days later a group of five colonists, including Ned and Thaddeus, arrived at the town of the Chickahominy with the trading goods. The boys resumed their friendship with Pocahontas, as though nothing out of the ordinary had happened. Later Ned told Smith that Pocahontas was positive her father had been involved in the attempted murder. She was heartbroken and sickened by her father's duplicity, but apparently knew none of the details.

The incident confirmed Smith's view that, no matter how friendly the Indians might seem, they could not be trusted. They were savages whose concepts of right and wrong, good and evil, and honor and trickery were primitive. His own policy of refusing to sell them firearms was dramatically vindicated.

Work on the house continued at a rapid, steady pace, even though several men stood guard duty night and day. At the end of another week of hard labor the structure was completed. Powhatan opened his warehouses for the meat and grain he had agreed to pay, and Smith obtained considerable additional stores after bartering with the sachem for the better part of a morning.

The settlers left for home that same afternoon, and the company was large enough for the English and Dutch colonists to carry the provisions themselves. Smith, after his close escape from death, wanted no warriors acting as bearers. Everyone was afraid the Chickahominy might try to ambush the party in the forest, so muskets and pistols were kept ready for instant use. Thaddeus and Ned marched at the head of the column with Smith, and were so thoroughly at home in the wilderness by now that they were occasionally sent ahead as scouts to see if the Chickahominy were setting a trap.

On January 22, 1609, John Smith had reason to feel satisfied with his accomplishments. The sight of the Jamestown palisades across the cornfields made him realize he was bringing back enough food to see the colony safely through the rest of the winter. In spite of the Indian's treachery, a costly war had been avoided, and he hoped to devote the coming months to preparations for the busiest spring in the colony's short history.

A tragic shock awaited him and his companions at the settlement. Matthew Scrivener, fearing the President's anger when Smith learned how generous he had been in doling out supplies, had fled from Jamestown two days earlier, taking eight men with him in the schooner. They had gone in the early hours of the morning, before dawn, while everyone else had been asleep. Their absence had not been discovered until some time after breakfast, when a gale had blown up, and several men had hurried down to the waterfront to make certain that the *Discovery* and the schooner were safely moored.

The evening prior to Smith's return a band of coastal Indians had come to Jamestown with the bodies of Scrivener and the unfortunate men he had persuaded to accompany him. The schooner had broken apart at sea in the storm; all nine men had been drowned, and their bodies had been washed ashore near the Indian village.

No one knew, or would know, whether Scrivener had hoped to sail across the Atlantic in the little craft or had planned to find a sanctuary of sorts somewhere on the North American coast.

Smith was stunned by the defection and tragic death of the man he had trusted and had made his deputy. His faith in his ability to understand the characters of others was shaken. And an inventory of the food supplies on hand soon made him realize that had he not brought back extra provisions, Jamestown might have starved in the spring.

The effect of Scrivener's death on the spirits of the colony was severe, and Smith prescribed his usual recipe, hard work. Although the weather was bitterly cold he assigned forty men the task of building a new, somewhat larger schooner. He placed Ratcliffe in nominal charge of the operation, as a sea captain should have known more than anyone else about the construction of a ship. But the long years of hardship in the wilderness had taken their toll, and Ratcliffe's mind had slipped. Sometimes he was alert and crafty, but without warning he occasionally mumbled and spoke incoherently. So Smith actually supervised the project himself.

Five days of driving rain melted the snow, and when the weather cleared, the temperature was unseasonably mild. Smith promptly took advantage of the fair weather to send all those not working on the new schooner to cut down trees, prepare lumber and clear additional fields for the planting of crops. Then, when the new schooner was finished, the carpenters started putting up cottages for the next immigrants who were expected. The newest members of the community grumbled, being unaccustomed to outdoor labor in winter, but those who were heard complaining were given extra duties.

"When spring comes," Smith said, "everyone in town except the hunters and fishermen will work at farming. I want nothing to interfere with our efforts to become self-sufficient."

There was a break in the usual routines when a large band of Indians who lived far to the south of Jamestown arrived unexpectedly. These savages had heard of the mirrors, knives and other items used by the Englishmen for trading purposes, and carried with them enough corn and meat and beans to feed a company of fifty for almost two months. Smith was delighted by the windfall, and the visiting savages were entertained royally.

At the same time, however, the lessons learned at the town of the Chickahominy were not forgotten. Heavily armed militiamen kept a close watch over the visitors during their entire stay of almost a week.

In late February the weather became cold again, and a heavy

snowstorm turned the forest white. Jamestown had to dig itself out, and that night the men of Jamestown tumbled into bed exhausted. Before dawn the following morning the Chesapeake and Pamunkey, knowing no one would expect them to attack when the snow was so deep, struck in force.

A nodding sentry in the Fort stared in disbelief when he saw dark figures climbing over the palisades. Forgetting that he was supposed to ring a bell in the event of danger, the militiaman fired his musket out of the nearest window.

Within a few moments men poured out of the cottages, carrying their firearms, and some literally came face to face with the Chesapeake vanguard that was trying to open the main gate and admit their cohorts. John Russell was one of the colonists in this party. He swiftly recovered from his surprise and showed the same mettle as a fighting man that he had displayed at the town of the Chickahominy. The young gentleman-adventurer called the other settlers in the vicinity to him and ordered the firing of a volley at close range.

About half the Chesapeake vanguard were either killed or wounded. The survivors, frustrated in their attempt to open the gate, hurled themselves at the colonists, and a fierce hand-to-hand fight developed. Smith, who saw what was happening, sent several other gentlemen-adventurers with twenty-five men to help Russell, then hurried to the Fort to take overall command.

Russell "fought like a demon," as Smith wrote in the official report he sent to England, and not one warrior in the Chesapeake vanguard escaped. Meanwhile the savages outside the palisade could hear the sounds of the fighting, but the high wall prevented them from seeing what was happening. So they withdrew to the forest to give themselves a breathing spell.

Smith had no intention of granting them a respite, however. Two of the Fort's big guns were already facing inland, in the direction of the forest, and their crews frantically loaded them. One cannonball crashed through the leafless trees, and was followed by another, which smashed several evergreens to kindling.

Dawn broke, and in the early morning light the colonists stationed in the observation tower of the Fort could see several hundred savages fleeing deeper into the wilderness. The brief battle was ended, with the Chesapeake sustaining the only casualties, seven warriors killed and thirty wounded.

The injured were held as prisoners, and Smith questioned them. Some, hoping for clemency, claimed that the Pamunkey had been responsible for the attack, and had persuaded the Chesapeake to join them. The warriors actually sounded almost completely innocent.

One of the wounded had sustained only a slight injury, and Smith sent him off with a message to his chief. The other braves would be held for a ransom of ten bushels of corn for each prisoner.

Jamestown shivered when it was realized how close the call had been. Had the sentry who gave the initial alarm dozed for as long as another minute or two, the gate would have been opened, and hundreds of savages would have poured through the town, burning, knifing and looting. Sentry rules were changed, and no fewer than three men were assigned to a given post at any one time.

A band of Chesapeake arrived within a week to ransom their comrades, and the wounded Indians were released in return for the corn, but everyone in Jamestown knew from the expressions on the faces of the sullen, humiliated Chesapeake that the tribe would not be content until her braves obtained revenge. Sooner or later they would return, and the colonists well knew it.

Early in the spring of 1609 there was still another crisis when it was discovered that a number of tools were missing from the storehouse. The Council investigated the matter, and eventually it was learned that a settler known to posterity only as Francis the Dutchman had taken axes and hammers, which he had traded to the coastal Indians for private supplies of food.

The savages had bartered in good faith, so Smith made no attempt to recover the stolen property. It was far better, he decided, to let the tribesmen keep the few tools than incur their ill will. Francis, however, could not be allowed to escape lightly. The Council held a special meeting, and it was decided by unanimous vote that the thief should receive twenty lashes with a cat-o'-nine-tails.

The whole community assembled on the parade ground. Attendance was obligatory for the men and boys, and only the two women were allowed to absent themselves. Francis was stripped to the waist and tied to a stake, with his hands chained around it. Each stroke of the whip sent a shudder through the crowd. When the punishment was completed, the prisoner, who had fallen unconscious, was examined by a physician before being carried off to the jail. The colonists were unusually silent and thoughtful as they went off to their cottages, and the Council members thought it unlikely that there would be additional difficulties with thieves in the near future.

Other problems remained. With the coming of warmer weather, spring planting began in earnest. Approximately two hundred acres were under cultivation. Farming tools were primitive and the work was exhausting. Those who toiled in the fields resented the hunters and fishermen, whose lot they considered easier. Several violent disputes erupted, but the Council restored order with a new decree. The field workers could apply for transfer to the fishing or hunting details, but would be penalized if they failed to bring in a prescribed quota. The complaints stopped.

After the crops were planted, work was resumed on the making of tar and pitch, and experiments were conducted to improve the quality of the glass the colonists manufactured. Men who knew good wood from mediocre went out into the forest to mark prime cedar and oak. These trees were felled, boards were fashioned, and then the lumber was stored in special sheds erected for the purpose. When the next ship arrived, Jamestown would be ready to send her products to England.

There was time now to make technical improvements, and Smith took full advantage of the unaccustomed leisure. Strong fishing nets were made, and traps were imbedded in the James River and its tributaries. A series of new blockhouses strengthened the palisade, and a deep well was dug at the Fort in order to make the place self-sustaining in the event of a siege. A smaller, auxiliary fort was also built on the river to protect shipping.

The experiment with wild hogs had proved surprisingly successful, and there was now a rapidly growing pig population that was expected to reach three figures by the end of the summer. There were five hundred chickens in pens, and fresh eggs had become commonplace, although the original settlers still regarded them as luxuries.

Sturgeon and shad ran in such great numbers all through the spring that vast numbers of the fish were smoked, and experiments also produced "sturgeon bread," a dish of the fish, cornmeal and herbs, which most of the people enjoyed. And oysters were so abundant in Chesapeake Bay that they were served, either roasted or fried, with every meal.

The health of the colony was remarkably good, the physicians having learned to use various forest herbs to cure sickness. Aside from the ill-fated Scrivener and his companions, only seven men had died during the winter, which was a new record. For the first time since the founding of the colony, evidence indicated that Jamestown was at last becoming self-sufficient, able to support herself.

Life had become so stable and prosperous that, by the middle of the colony's third summer in the New World, Captain John Smith was able to start thinking again of his real love, exploration. After his experience with Scrivener, there was no one man to whom he could entrust the affairs of Jamestown, so he thought it better to leave the settlement in the hands of several men who would share authority as equals.

Making his preparations carefully, he began to plan a new, extensive trip into the interior that would reveal more of the wilderness' secrets to civilized man.

XII

IN MID-JULY, 1609, John Smith and a small group of companions set out in the new schooner to sail up the James River, explore its headwaters and penetrate as far as they could into the wilderness beyond. Jamestown was peaceful and prosperous, and Smith left precise orders for the harvesting of crops, should they ripen before his return. He had no reason to expect that grave problems would arise during his absence.

Soon after his departure from Jamestown, however, the trouble started. It began when a small ship commanded by Captain Samuel Argal arrived from England. Argal, who carried neither immigrants nor supplies for the settlers, had been granted a special permit by the colony's sponsors in England to search for the mythical gold and gems that the great lords still sought. Argal was a brusk, cruel man, contemptuous of authority, who refused to obey any of Jamestown's regulations. He soon became friendly with Gabriel Archer, and together they set a bad example for the industrious, hard-working people of the little colony.

Argal's sailors were almost as bad as their superior. Undisciplined brawlers, they intimidated the colonists. Then, indifferent to the laws governing trade with the Indians, they not only went off on their own to barter with the savages, but cheated the Chesapeake so viciously in trades that the already hostile tribe now had a double grievance against the colony.

The colonists saw Argal and his men sleeping until noon, playing cards until late at night and doing no work. Many decided to follow their example, and the ripening crops were neglected. Fisherman were often too lazy to go out to sea, and hunters found excuses to remain at home. The Council tried to enforce discipline, but there were so many law-breakers that the gentlemen-adventurers felt helpless.

Former President Ratcliffe, who had seemed harmless for many months, soon proved he was still capable of creating mischief. He did as he pleased, refusing to work, and many of the colonists, including Ned and Thaddeus, believed he had found some way to break into the storehouse again and steal food for himself. He proved so cunning, however, that the charges against him could not be substantiated.

Gradually the rations were increased, the members of the Council becoming careless. And, with more food being used than was being gathered, the provisions dwindled at a rapid rate. Coastal Indians warned the colonists that the Chesapeake and Pamunkey were planning to launch a major military campaign against the settlement, but the threat failed to develop, and the Council members slowly became convinced that the alarm was false.

Archer, still hoping to win public approval and supplant Smith as President, went off on a visit to the Chickahominy. He disdainfully ignored the prohibition of Smith and Captain Newport that had been laid down in Jamestown's earliest days, and he traded firearms for corn and venison. Apparently it did not occur to him that he was giving the savages weapons which, in time, might enable them to drive the Englishmen into the sea.

Smith, who had been elected to a second term as President before his departure, had no idea that all he had fought to accomplish was being destroyed by thoughtless, selfish men. While he was sailing his schooner to falls high on the James River, then marching overland and mapping a vast area, the greedy were pulling down the structure he had erected with such great effort and care. While he was establishing friendly relations with Indian tribes who had never before seen an Englishman, others were creating hatreds, making new enemies of the savages already familiar with the settlers.

After spending many weeks in the interior, Smith at last started back toward the coast. The deck of the schooner was piled high with corn and venison, he had made another significant contribution to civilization's knowledge of the New World, and he felt content. The forest no longer kept any secrets from him, and was his ally rather than his foe.

Then, suddenly, he was badly burned when the bag of gunpowder exploded on the deck of the schooner.

The other members of the party crowded on as much sail as the schooner could carry. They did what they could to care for him, spreading deer suet on his burns. But, as they well knew, their efforts were inadequate. Twice Smith regained consciousness for brief periods, but did not complain, even though his agony was excruciating.

When the schooner finally arrived at Jamestown, he was in a coma.

The news spread quickly, and virtually the whole town gathered in a somber silence to watch him being carried to the President's house. There the community's two physicians went to work, placing poultices of a healing ointment on his burns. When he next became conscious they gave him an elixir of herbs to drink, and although it did nothing to cure his condition, his pain was somewhat relieved.

For six days and nights he was at the point of death. One or the other of the physicians remained at his side, and the Reverend Hunt did not leave his bedchamber. Finally, after being in a critical condition for almost a week, Smith improved slightly and became lucid.

As soon as he regained his senses he began to inquire about conditions in the colony. The clergyman, not wanting to excite him, tried to evade his questions. But Smith was insistent, and the Reverend Hunt felt compelled to tell him the truth. Smith immediately sent for his Council, even though the physicians warned him he might suffer a relapse.

Before the day ended, John Smith learned the truth about Jamestown's deplorable state. He was so exhausted he fell asleep for a few hours, but a mug of chicken broth seemed to revive him after he regained consciousness, and he summoned the Council again.

That was the start of the strangest month in Jamestown's short but spectacular history. The mind and will of one man, an invalid incapable of rising from his sick bed, prevented the total collapse of the first English colony in North America.

At Smith's direction the crops were harvested and the soil prepared for the following spring's planting.

Hunting and fishing parties were sent out on double shifts, and worked day and night to make up for lost time.

Although it was impossible to regain possession of the firearms Gabriel Archer had sold to the Chickahominy, Archer himself was placed under arrest and put in jail.

Hidden provisions were found in the house of former President Ratcliffe. He, too, was sent to jail, protesting his innocence.

Captain Samuel Argal was called to Smith's bedchamber, and the bully's bravado suddenly collapsed. No matter what rights he had been granted by the royal patent holders in London, Smith told him, he was required to obey the laws of Jamestown, which were the King's law. Argal was given two choices: he could either obey or leave.

Not realizing the moral strength of the crippled, heavily bandaged man in the bed, Argal tried to bluster.

Smith was prepared for just such a reaction. John Russell and two other young gentlemen-adventurers were waiting in the adjoining room, and came in quickly when the President called to them in a weak voice. If Argal and his men refused to behave, he said, the militia was directed to destroy their ship and drive the troublemakers into the forest at musket point.

Argal saw that Smith meant business, and changed his tune. He begged for another chance, and it was given to him on the understanding that if he or his men caused any more difficulties, they would be sent into the wilderness to starve.

The most critical of the problems still unsolved was that of preventing war with the Chesapeake and Pamunkey. Smith worked out a bold, unorthodox plan. Since Ned and Thaddeus were now expert in speaking the language of the savages, he sent them, with a small escort, to visit the two tribes. Carefully following his instructions, they told the sachems of the Chesapeake and Pamunkey that Jamestown was offering them peace for the last time. If they refused, an expedition would be sent to their towns, and the huge cannon of the Englishmen would destroy their homes and grain fields.

The two boys carried out their orders to the letter. The Indians had no way of knowing that it would be literally impossible to carry the heavy guns emplaced at the fort on an expedition into the field. Thaddeus and Ned had learned to speak with grave, expressionless faces in the approved Indian manner, and their supreme bluff was effective. The two savage nations decided to make peace with the settlers. Once again Smith proved himself a master in the art of dealing with primitive people, this time aided by two boys who were his able pupils.

So the colony was safe and order was restored. But no one was able to estimate the personal cost to Smith. His condition took a turn for the worse, and the physicians knew of no way to save his life.

Then, unexpectedly, Captain Newport reappeared at the head of the largest squadron of ships Jamestown had ever seen, the

Susan Constant leading the *Lion,* the *Falcon,* the *Unity* and the *Blessing.* All were heavily laden with supplies, and all carried scores of immigrants. The population of Jamestown was literally doubled overnight.

Newport, shocked by Smith's condition, could think only of the patient's health, and ordered two new physicians who were members of the landing party to attend him. Among the supplies were various medicines, and for the first time Smith obtained genuine relief from his pain.

When he was feeling more comfortable, Newport told him news that was almost too good to believe. The sponsors of Jamestown had finally accepted Smith's views and had given up their dreams of finding gold and diamonds in Virginia. Instead they were making an increased effort to establish a permanent colony in the New World.

The four ships in the squadron that had just arrived comprised the vanguard of a much larger group. In all, nine other vessels were following, some of them the largest in the British merchant fleet. Smith's advice was being taken literally, and the new colonists were bringing with them all they would need to establish roots in the wilderness. In the holds were the most modern plows, and on the decks were horses to pull them, as well as cattle, sheep and other livestock.

Taking Smith at his word, the investors had recruited with care, and most of the new immigrants were either farmers or expert artisans. All were sober, hard-working men anxious to create lives for themselves in America. Some brought their wives and children with them, and there were also dozens of unmarried women among the passengers. The days of an almost exclusively bachelor community were at an end.

The flotilla was also bringing Jamestown new cannon,

enough muskets to arm every settler, and ample supplies of shot and gunpowder. Kegs were filled with wheat, barley, oats and vegetable seeds, and there were enough of the items the Indians liked to satisfy the savages for years to come.

Smith was completely vindicated, yet he was not happy. Never one to fool himself, he knew his health was too precarious for him to administer the affairs of the enlarged community. Although it grieved him to think of leaving America, he realized he needed rest, medical care and a long convalescence in England if he hoped to recover.

Again Newport reassured him. The colonization of Virginia had become such an important enterprise that the crown was sending one of the most able men in the realm, Lord De La Warr, to Jamestown as Governor. He would arrive with the main fleet, accompanied by a staff of competent assistants. It had been the hope of Lord De La Warr and of the colony's sponsors that Smith would remain as his deputy and military commander. But, as that was impossible, Smith could return to England knowing he would be replaced by a man of real stature capable of governing the colony efficiently.

Relieved of his burden at last, Smith gratefully agreed to sail back to England on the *Susan Constant.* Newport, taking temporary charge, deported Archer and Ratcliffe on other vessels.

Houses were being erected at a furious rate for the new arrivals, and the sound of axes felling trees, of hammers ringing and of the unaccustomed bustle that broke the deep silence of the forest disturbed Smith, keeping him awake. The physicians felt he would rest more comfortably on board ship, so he was moved to the *Susan Constant,* Newport relinquishing his own quarters to his friend for the voyage.

One more vessel arrived by the time Newport was ready to
sail in mid-October, bringing word that the other ships would
reach port in three or four weeks. Newport, thinking primarily
of his distinguished passenger's health, was reluctant to wait,
knowing that the Atlantic would become rougher, week by
week, as winter approached. So his hold was loaded with some
of the goods that Smith had prepared months earlier, and Newport made ready to sail.

On the day of departure John Smith was carried onto the
main deck of the *Susan Constant,* and reclined on a couch that
the carpenters had made for him in their spare time. There he
could gaze, for the last time, at the Fort, the church, the thatched
roofs of the cottages, the palisade and, beyond the town, the
dark, ever present forest.

The settlers came on board to bid him farewell and wish him
Godspeed. They formed in a line and, at the direction of the
physicians, spoke only a few words to him, not pausing as they
moved past the couch.

But Smith himself raised a hand when Ned and Thaddeus
appeared, and he halted the boys, a slow smile spreading across
his gaunt face. "You were children when we first came here,"
he said to them, "and now you'll soon be men. You know
the forest and the savages. In fact, you're almost as dark as the
Indians. You've learned how to live off the land that can be the
most bountiful on earth when she is respected. Stay here, lads.
Make your homes here. The future belongs to you."

Thaddeus and Ned were so overwhelmed that they stood,
tears in their eyes, unable to reply.

A short time later the settlers went ashore, and everyone
waved and cheered as the *Susan Constant* weighed anchor. John
Smith raised a limp hand in return, and his own eyes were

moist as he looked for the last time at the people, the forest, and the town that he, more than any other person, had created.

History seldom arranges happy endings for its real-life heroes and heroines, but there are exceptions.

Captain John Smith eventually enjoyed a complete recovery from his burns, and his physicians in London attributed the miracle to the superb physical condition he had attained in wilderness living. His exploits in Jamestown made him one of England's most famous men, and his renown was further enhanced by the publication of his books and maps. He became the intimate friend of many great lords, and a close associate of Archdeacon Hakluyt. He was on the best of terms, too, with Prince Henry, until the untimely death of the heir to the throne.

Smith did not return to Jamestown, which continued to grow. He felt there was no need for him there. But the forests of the New World and a yearning for exploration were in his blood, and in 1614 he commanded an expedition of his own to more Northern waters. He landed in the vicinity of what later became Portsmouth, New Hampshire, and claimed the whole of the vast northern seaboard for King James. Sailing up and down the coast, he discovered virtually all of New England, from Maine to Connecticut, and gave New England its name. Even more notable than his new explorations were the maps he drew of the coast. They were so accurate that, like his maps of Chesapeake Bay and Virginia, they were used for the better part of two hundred years.

In the next two years Smith made other, somewhat less spectacular voyages, but continued to increase the store of mankind's knowledge of the New World.

Early in 1617, as a reward for his services and in recognition of his achievements, he was granted the title of Admiral of New England.

Meantime, in Virginia, a little Indian girl who had once saved his life had grown to womanhood. Pocahontas visited Jamestown often, her desire to become a convert grew stronger, and she finally took the great step, the first Indian in what was later the United States to become a Christian.

At Jamestown, too, Pocahontas met a young man with whom she fell in love. John Rolfe was a widower with two small children, a handsome, dynamic man who shared John Smith's passionate conviction that the real wealth of the New World lay in her soil. Rolfe knew that the Indians grew tobacco for their own use, and as pipe smoking was spreading in Europe, he began to cultivate tobacco on a large scale. His was the first real tobacco plantation in North America, and his hard work was crowned with such success that he became known as the "father of the tobacco industry."

He returned Pocahontas' affection, and they were married in the little Jamestown church that Smith had built for the Reverend Hunt. The ceremony, which was probably performed in 1616, sealed the bond between the settlers and the Chickahominy Confederation. Never again during the reign of Powhatan, or subsequently, that of Pocahontas' brother, Opachisco, were relations between the English colonists and the savages marred by war or the threat of war.

The son of Pocahontas and Rolfe was born in Jamestown in 1617, and later that same year the family paid a visit to England, where they were guests of Lord and Lady De La Warr, who had themselves returned from Virginia. Pocahontas created an overnight sensation in London. People were curious because she was an Indian princess and a convert to Christianity, but mere inquisitiveness soon gave way to sheer admiration. Everyone at the court of James I was dazzled by Pocahontas' charm and intellect. She soon became an intimate friend of Queen Anne, and visited the Queen daily. Prince Charles, the younger son of James and Anne, who had become Prince of Wales on the death of his brother, Henry, and who was only a few years younger than Pocahontas, developed an interest in the New World after hearing her speak of the wilderness.

Perhaps the greatest surprise of Pocahontas' visit to London was her ability to converse fluently and learnedly with the great scholars who were preparing a new translation of the Bible for King James. As these clergymen and professors of Hebrew and Greek readily admitted, her knowledge of the Bible was as great as their own. Even the dour King James fell under Pocahontas' spell; he frequently granted audiences to her and Rolfe and astonished his courtiers by relaxing and laughing, something he rarely did when in the company of his own nobles.

Captain John Smith was spending most of his time in western England, where he was deeply involved in complicated financial matters preliminary to the formation of a new company that would colonize New England. But he returned to London before the visit of Pocahontas and Rolfe came to an end, and had his first meeting with them at a reception given by Lord and Lady De La Warr.

When the graying Smith entered the ballroom of the mansion, Pocahontas immediately broke away from the group with whom she was speaking and went to him.

Smith bent low to kiss her hand, and she impulsively embraced him. Laughing, they stepped back to look at each other, and the years fell away. Pocahontas was no longer the lovely matron in a gown of yellow and crimson silk, but a little Indian girl in a shabby dress of woven reeds. And Smith was no longer a distinguished, middle-aged gentleman, but a daring young adventurer whose life she had just saved.

"I envy you," he said to her. "I doubt that I'll ever leave England again, but you'll soon be going home—to the forest. It's my home, too, until the day I die."

Afterword

It is one of the ironies of history that Pocahontas did not see her homeland again and that Jamestown, as a community, crumbled away in John Smith's lifetime.

The fate of the Indian princess was tragic and harsh. The raw English weather proved fatal to a young woman accustomed to a gentler climate, and Pocahontas died shortly before she and her husband were scheduled to return to Virginia. John Rolfe buried her in a churchyard at Gravesend, where her tombstone may still be seen.

The village known as Jamestown knew its greatest glory under John Smith, and although the sponsors of the colony sent recruits by the hundreds to the settlement, they did not remain there. Most of the newcomers preferred to fan out into the rich farm country of the Virginia hinterland, and there, secure because of the work Smith had done in creating an English colony, they sank their roots.

The town itself was situated on lowland ground harmful to health, and those who followed the early settlers realized it. Although the first representative government in North America was organized in Jamestown in 1619, its population continued to dwindle. At the peak of John Smith's Presidency there were nearly five hundred persons living in Jamestown. By 1623 the number dwindled to 183, and thereafter became still smaller.

The colonists thought the place so insignificant that no other census was ever taken.

The original buildings were preserved for a time, but many rotted and were destroyed by the elements. Virginia was flourishing, and Jamestown had already served its noble purpose. Most of the structures still standing were burned to the ground in a fire that broke out, by accident, during the rebellion of Nathaniel Bacon and his followers in 1676. But by that time Virginia had taken her place as the leader of the English-speaking colonies, a position she was destined to hold for a long time. George Washington and Patrick Henry, Thomas Jefferson, James Madison and James Monroe were direct inheritors of the traditions established by Captain John Smith and his brave men, who learned how to survive in the wilderness of the New World.

Bibliography

Brown, Alexander, *Genesis of the United States*, Cambridge, Mass., 1890.

Chatterton, E. K., *Captain John Smith*, John Lane, London, 1927.

Doyle, J. A., *English in America*, New York, 1881–82.

Fiske, John, *Old Virginia and Her Neighbors*, New York, 1897.

Green, John R., *A Short History of the English People*, London, 1895.

Lewis, Paul, *The Great Rogue, A Biography of John Smith*, David McKay Co., New York, 1966.

Neill, Edward D., *English Colonization of America*, London, 1871.

————, *Virginia Company in London*, London, 1869.

Smith, John, *A Description of New England*, London, 1615.

————, *A Map of Virginia, with a Description of the Country*, Oxford, 1612.

————, *The General History of Virginia, New England and the Summer Isles*, London, 1624.

Warner, Charles D., *John Smith*, New York, 1881.

Wharton, Henry, *The Life of John Smith*, translated from the Latin and with an essay by Laura Polanyi Striker, University of North Carolina Press, Chapel Hill, N.C., 1957.

INDEX

188